Poverty and Plenty
on the Turkish Farm

**A Study of Income Distribution
in Turkish Agriculture**

Eva Hirsch

**Modern Middle East Series
No. 1**

**Published by
The Middle East Institute of Columbia
Distributed by
Columbia University Press, New York**

TABLE OF CONTENTS

LIST OF TABLES

This study began as an attempt to ascertain what effect economic development in Turkey has had on income distribution. As a first step in the research the author attempted to estimate income distribution in the agricultural and non-agricultural sectors. After this work had progressed for some time, it became apparent that the project undertaken was a more extensive one than had been anticipated because of the difficulties involved in obtaining reliable statistics. To make the work manageable, it was decided to make separate estimates of income distribution in the agricultural and in the non-agricultural sectors. When the first of these estimates was completed, it had become so extensive because of the large number of problems encountered in analyzing the data, that it was decided to write up the results of the estimate on income distribution in agriculture as a separate study, which I submitted as my Ph.D. dissertation at Columbia University, and to finish the remainder of the project at a later time. (In the meantime, in collaboration with Abraham Hirsch, I have completed work on several other phases of the original broader project, and the results have been published in separate articles.)*

---

*Eva Hirsch and Abraham Hirsch, "Changes in Agricultural Output per Capita of Rural Population in Turkey, 1927-60," Economic Development and Cultural Change, Vol. XI, No. 4 (July 1963); "Changes in Terms of Trade of Farmers and Their Effect on Real Farm Income per Capita of Rural Population in Turkey, 1927-60," ibid., Vol. XIV, No. 4 (July 1966); "Tax Reform and the Burden of Direct Taxation in Turkey," Public Finance/Finances Publiques, Vol. XXI, No. 3, (1966).

This book represents for the most part a revised version of my dissertation. Some of the estimates have been recomputed to take account of additional information that has become available since the dissertation was written-- although it should be pointed out that none of these changes has significantly altered any conclusions previously derived--and some of the detail included in the original version has been omitted in the interest of readability. The main new material consists of an estimate of the distribution of income earned by each tenth of farm families from both agricultural and non-agricultural sources. The new distribution has been added because I believe that a size distribution of income has greater significance if it refers to the total income of the families in question, and my earlier findings on income distribution had included only agricultural incomes. The broader distribution as well as the new estimates of the distribution of non-agricultural incomes that farmers earn, which had to be made for this purpose, have been added to Chapter IX.

The estimates in this book refer to the years 1951-1953. This period was chosen because of the relatively large amount of usable statistical material available for these years, including detailed published information on Turkish national income and its derivation, as well as three valuable statistical studies in the field of Turkish agriculture. Most important, a relatively large portion of these statistics proved to be of usable quality (or could be made usable by adjusting for biases) so that estimates based on these data could be expected to produce meaningful results.

In doing the research I have received more assistance than I could hope to acknowledge. A great many persons have given me valuable help in supplying me with unpublished statistics or with background information needed to clarify the meaning of statistical data.

My special thanks are due to Professors Reşat
Aktan, Marvel Baker, George Brandow, Ömer Celal
Sarç, Doçent Sabahaddin Zaim, Dr. Hasan Lay,
the late Mr. Şefik Bilkur, Miss Piraye Bigat,
Messrs. Vedat Eldem, Nafiz Erus, Mustafa
Fotozoğlu, Nejat Iren, Feridun Kurtkan, Hakki
Özkazanç, and Kemal Togay.

     I owe a debt, too, to Professor A. R.
Burns, my dissertation advisor, for his guid-
ance and valuable criticism, and to my husband,
Abraham Hirsch, for the hours spent in discus-
sing the many difficulties encountered in the
research and for having helped me in more ways
than I could enumerate. Larry Lowenthal,
Katharine Kosmak, and Alma Routsong have been
most helpful with the final editing and
conscientious clerical assistance. Finally,
I gratefully acknowledge a grant from the
Rutgers Research Council for revising the
typescript for publication.

CHAPTER I

INTRODUCTION

I. <u>Some Characteristics of Turkish Agriculture</u>

A. <u>Rainfall</u>

The Anatolian peninsula, which comprises 97 percent of the area of the country, consists for most part of a semi-arid plateau. Mountains separate the plateau from the seas which wash the shores of the peninsula in the North, West, and South, and although the sea winds collect a considerable amount of moisture while crossing the water, the mountains cause the winds to discharge much of their moisture over the mountain slopes before they move inland. As a result the interior plateau receives very little rainfall.

About a third of the crop area of the country is located between the mountains and the seas, the other two thirds comprise the semi-arid plateau.[1] The coastal regions are relatively humid, particularly the Black Sea region in the north, comprising 7 percent of the nation's crop area, where the mountains leave in most areas only a very narrow coastal strip. Here the winds can hardly penetrate inland before the mountains cause them to discharge their moisture over this narrow strip. In consequence the Black Sea region receives an unusually large amount of precipitation. The other coastal regions receive less moisture, but, on the whole, an adequate amount.[2]

Most peasants are self-sufficient to a considerable extent. When rainfall is plentiful and the crop good, a part of it is sold. But in dry years there may be nothing left beyond what is needed to satisfy the immediate needs of the family. This near-self-sufficient character of

Turkish agriculture, together with the dryness
of most of the country, determines the main crops
grown. Cereals are important to the self-sufficient farmer, and small grains have a superior
ability to withstand dryness. As a result small-
grain cereals are the main crops of the country,
and among these wheat and barley predominate.[3]
Wheat constitutes the main food crop and is made
into bread, and barley and most other grains are
used for feed. Most wheat is sown in the fall,
as the particular distribution of rainfall on
the plateau allows autumn-sown crops to receive
a greater amount of moisture. Barley, which requires less rainfall, is sown in the spring.
In the interior very little is grown besides
cereals, and in the more humid coastal areas
these crops are also important, though less
predominant.[4] The coastal areas also produce
Turkey's well-known export crops, such as tobacco, cotton, raisins, nuts, figs, etc. These
cash crops generally yield a much higher return
than do the grains.

Crop output is very unstable. Yields
fluctuate from year to year depending on the
amount of rainfall during the growing seasons.[5]
In years of heavy rainfall the semi-arid parts
of the plateau may shrink to small islands, but
in drought years they encompass whole regions.[6]
During a poor year wheat yields in some of the
dry provinces may be one fourth or less of those
in good years.[7] Yields fluctuate also in the
coastal areas, but not as violently as in the
semi-arid ones. To insulate themselves against
disaster, peasants typically keep on hand considerable stocks of wheat.[8] The violent changes
in Turkey's crop output therefore do not indicate equally large changes in the food supply,
although consumption seems to vary with size of
crops, especially when several good or poor years
succeed one another.[9]

B. Institutional Characteristics

(1) Land tenure and farm size. The
Turkish village population consists of three million families, averaging about six members each,[10]
who live in some 38,000 villages.[11] Arable land
in Turkey is privately owned, but grazing land
is owned in common by the village. Ownership of
arable land is widely dispersed. Of the families
who operate farms (excluding landless families)
74 percent own their farms, 22 percent are part
owners, and only 4 percent work on fully rented
farms.[12] About 12 percent of all village families do not operate any land,[13] and of these the
greater part are occupied as year-round agricultural laborers.[14] Although most peasants own
their farms the average farm is very small. The
mean holding consists of nineteen acres, but the
median holding is only about ten acres, and the
modal holding about five acres.[15]

(2) Methods of production. Methods of
production are primitive and do not enable the
average peasant to get as large an income from
his small plot as he might. Artificial fertilizer is used only to a negligible extent, and
in the treeless parts of the semi-arid plateau
not even animal manure is returned to the soil
since it must serve as fuel for cooking and
heating in the absence of other sources. As a
result, on the average only two thirds of the
land can be cultivated every year. One third
must be left fallow to permit the soil to re-
store its nutrients.[16]

The land is generally worked with wooden
plows, pulled by a pair of underfed and under-
sized oxen or water buffalos. These animals are
very slow and generally not able to work the
land in time to get optimum yields. The plowing
season is very short. In the fall the wooden
plows cannot penetrate the soil until the first

rains soften the ground, but sowing must be finished in time to allow the seedlings to take root before the onset of frost. Similarly if done in the spring, plowing must wait till the frost leaves the ground, but must be early enough not to bring the seedlings too close to the dry summer season.[17] With the slow draft animals, plowing and sowing can generally not be done at the optimum time, and when the weather is unfavorable and shortens the period available for these tasks, yields are much lower than when the work can be done in time.[18] All of this is apart from the amount of rainfall during the growing season. Yields are very much dependent on rainfall, as already noted, but also depend on timeliness of plowing, and the draft power of the average farmer is, except in unusual years, inadequate.

To remedy the shortage of draft power, some 30,000 tractors were imported into the country between 1948 and 1952[19] and by 1952 about 14 percent of the area cultivated in Turkey was worked with mechanical equipment.[20] The tractors have helped to increase the yields of the mechanized, mostly large farmers, but the hopes that small farmers too might use tractors through cooperative or village ownership have not materialized.[21] Not only has the mechanization program not helped the small farmer, it has helped to increase the size of the large farms and reduce the number of small ones. Tractors are typically operated by the land owners themselves so that tenants were sometimes evicted when tractors were introduced.[22] Moreover, because tractors could cultivate more land than that operated by many tractor owners, these relatively large farmers have bought and rented still additional land, in many cases from the peasants.[23] Thus the introduction of tractors increased output, but did not help the small farmer, and led to the eviction of some former tenants.

(3) <u>Animals</u>. Crop land constitutes the main source from which the livelihood of the Turkish peasant is derived. But income from animal products constitutes an important additional source, although this income, too, is smaller than it would be if more scientific methods were used. Selective breeding is not practiced, and the pastures are heavily overgrazed. Though privately owned, animals are grazed together on common land belonging to the villages, i.e., land encompassed by the village boundaries that is not considered suitable for cultivation. The average farmer, besides owning two oxen which provide his draft power has, in addition, eight sheep, six goats, and two cows.[24] These provide him primarily with milk and wool and increase his income by a substantial proportion.[25] Their importance as a source of agricultural income is greatest in the eastern parts of the country.

(4) <u>Seasonal employment and migration</u>. The work connected with crops and animals keeps the peasant busy during only part of the year. There is much work to be done during the plowing seasons, both in the fall and spring, which last about one and one half months each. Not only does the land have to be plowed for the crops to be sown, but if time permits, the fallow should be plowed, too, as this enables more moisture to be retained in the soil. There is in addition a hectic month-and-a-half to two-months period during harvest time when men, women, and children must help and no hands can be spared. Besides these three main seasons there are other periods of less pressing activity. During perhaps four to six months of the year, however, there is little if any farm work to be done.

During the slack seasons many small peasants try to supplement their incomes by seeking wage work, either in industry and mines or in agriculture. Such seasonal agricultural work usually involves temporary migration to other regions of the country for, unless the peasant has a farm so small that he has time to spare during the active seasons, there is little opportunity for agricultural employment in the same village or area, since within each region the slack seasons and the active seasons on large and small farms, on the whole, coincide. At the time when labor is needed on the large farms in the area--mostly for harvest work--the small peasant (except the smallest) is fully busy with his own harvest. The situation differs between regions; in different regions different crops are grown and even for the same crops the harvesting period may come at a different time of the year. Therefore many farmers are able to migrate temporarily to other regions to do agricultural work and yet return to their villages in time to help with the harvest at home.

Farm labor is not the only source of supplementary income to small peasants. As mentioned above, there is also temporary work done in towns and in mining areas, and in addition peasants' incomes are supplemented by non-agricultural work done in villages, of which the most important is household industry.

C. Classes and Function

It is seen from what has been said above that there are no separate classes of landlords and tenants in Turkey. The typical cultivator is a peasant proprietor, and while there are some landless families, their proportion is relatively small. Thus, the difference between the rich cultivator and the poor, for the most part, is that the former owns a lot of land, and perhaps one or more tractors, while the latter owns very little land. Both small and large farmers rent land, the former because he does not have enough land to make a living; the latter because he can better exploit his tractor if he

has more land. The vast majority of cultivators
perform all the traditional functions, i.e.,
they contribute land, capital, and labor, and
most income is therefore imputed income. This
creates some difficulties in estimating functional shares, as will be seen in the next chapter.

II. Statistics Used

A. Some Problems Encountered in Working with Turkish Statistics

Compared with those in many other underdeveloped countries Turkish statistics are rather
extensive. While most underdeveloped countries
launched consciously planned government attempts
at economic improvement only after World War II,
Turkey began as early as the lat 1920's, and on
a broader scale in the 1930's. For these pro-
grams statistics were needed, and the Central
Statistical Office was set up at an early date
to bring together statistical material obtained
by other agencies and to make its own surveys.
As a result a rather large amount of statistical
information is available in Turkey, although some
fields are covered more fully than others, and
some not at all.

Working with Turkish statistics, however,
presents a number of problems. Many statistics
are not published and it is difficult to find out
what data are available.[26] Published statistics
are generally not easy to work with. Headings
of tables, for example, do not always clearly
show what the data refer to. Very few of the
published data are accompanied by footnotes or
explanations on how the data were derived, and
usually these explanations are not so full as to
enable the reader to judge precisely what the
figures mean.[27]

Another important problem concerns the
accuracy of the data. It is generally believed
that the margin of error of some of the statis-

tics is rather wide because of problems encountered in gathering, tabulating, and publishing
data in Turkey, as it is generally in underdeveloped countries. So far as gathering statistics is concerned, it is often difficult to obtain correct information because of the suspicion
respondents have that in giving true answers they
will invite adverse government action. In agriculture, for example, experts in the 1950's expressed the view that peasants as a rule did not
disclose the correct number of animals they own,
apparently because of the existence of an animal
tax which many tried to evade. Even if assured
that the information will not be disclosed to
the tax authorities, many peasants remained sus-
picious. A similar problem exists in industry
where profits or value of assets are generally
believed to be under-reported. Since taxes are
or could be levied on any number of things, there
is a great deal of information that respondents
might find it wise to under-report.

The problem does not lie only in the at-
titude of the respondents. There is much difficulty in obtaining enough trained personnel to
carry out a survey. Well-trained statisticians
are few in a poor country and those few are
hardly enough to design and coordinate the over-
all survey. In addition a large staff is needed
for most surveys to do the interviewing, tabulating, etc., and the interviewers generally can get
only a very brief period of training. All too
often they have not been able to grasp the importance of some of the basic principles they
are supposed to follow. For example, if the
survey is to be a random one, it makes just as
much sense to an untrained person to go to the
next house if the resident of the designated
dwelling happens to be absent. It makes still
more sense to always include the village head,
since his cooperation in connection with a village survey is needed, and excluding him might
appear to signify insufficient respect.

There are also problems involved in
processing the data. In published statistics
one finds errors or misprints, shown up, for
example, when like series do not agree or when
figures do not add up to the total given. Shortage of funds for statistical work and shortage
of well-trained personnel are the main reasons
for these lacks. Even where very well-qualified
people are found, they do not generally have
the staff which is needed to do the job.

Considering all the problems that could
affect the accuracy of the Turkish data, most,
though not all, of the Turkish statistics turn
out to be much more usable than one would expect.
Various methods can be used to determine how usable they are. First, it is possible to obtain
information on how the data were gathered and
precisely what they refer to. The author has
spent a good deal of time while in Turkey talking
to government officials and statisticians who
were in charge of coordinating and processing
statistics. These persons are generally aware
of the type of information that respondents try
to conceal, and are also exceedingly helpful in
supplying all the information that is needed to
understand precisely what the data refer to.

In addition to learning how the data have
been put together, it is possible to check whether data are internally consistent, e.g., whether
sums add up to parts, whether an increase in one
area is also reflected in another, if that is
what should be expected. Moreover, it is possible
to subject some statistics to "tests of consilience,"[28] i.e., to find out whether a conclusion
reached by means of one set of figures is supported by other independently derived data. This
cannot be done with all statistics, but it can be
done for a number. For some statistics these
tests have raised serious questions as to accuracy
or interpretation, but the greater number passed
these tests quite well, i.e., the differences
were within margins of error that were not so

large as to upset the conclusions. These tests
will be discussed in the chapters where the statistics are used and in Appendices C and E.

B. The Main Sources of Data Used

        While a great many sources were used to
derive the estimates made in this study, three
sources have been particularly relied upon. One
is the 1952 Fall Survey[29] of the distribution of
land operated, which forms one of the main bases
for the estimates made in Part II below. In Appendix E these data are described and critically
evaluated. In addition two other studies have
been relied upon throughout the succeeding chapters and will briefly be described at this point.
        The most important single source used in
this book is an unpublished study done on incomes and costs of peasant families in Central
Anatolia, which will hereafter be referred to as
the Village Study. This study not only contains
a wealth of detailed information on types of
crops grown, yields, revenues from animal products, costs of labor, rent, etc., but in addition, the data are presented separately for farms
of different sizes, an invaluable source for a
study on income distribution.
        The study is based on a survey done in
the fall of 1953 under the direction of George
E. Brandow of the Foreign Operations Administration of the U.S.A.,[30] and included 500 farm families chosen at random in 100 villages distributed over the greater part of Central Anatolia.[31]
It seems to be of remarkably good quality, although the survey ran into the usual difficulties
of having to use relatively untrained personnel,
etc. Wherever possible the results of the study
were checked against independently derived information, and most of these tests have shown that
the data in the study checked remarkably well with
the other sources. There are, however, two main
exceptions. For one, the study includes relatively too many large farms compared with the

ratio of large and small farms in the nation.
This happened because many of the enumerators
did not understand the meaning of a random sample, and did not follow instruction as care-
fully as they should have. The examples cited
above that some enumerators would always include
the village heads--and these are generally the
larger land owners--derive from the experience
with this survey.[32] The second main area where
the statistics in the Village Study do not check
with the information derived from other sources
is in the relative importance of incomes from
animal products compared with the importance of
incomes from crops. As is pointed out in Appendix C, the main error in this instance lies in
the data with which the Village Study is compared, rather than in the animal statistics in
the Village Study itself.

The other important source for the estimates is a survey, Economic and Social Aspects
of Farm Mechanization, which will subsequently
be referred to as the Mechanization Study.[33] It
is based on a survey conducted in 1952 by a committee of the Faculty of Political Science at
Ankara University, sponsored by the Foreign Operations Administration of the U.S.A. The study
is highly significant for present purposes because mechanization has increased the incomes of
the relatively large farmers and therefore has
had an important bearing on income distribution,
and because it contains a wealth of statistics
that make it possible to gauge these effects in
detail.

The study is based on a rather large sample of 3,015 mechanized farms, which together
owned somewhat more than 10 percent of all tractors used in the nation at that time. The size
of this sample should make for relatively good
estimates of the population parameters, and in
addition, the study seems to have been well conducted. It has one shortcoming, however. The
regional distribution of the mechanized farms in
the sample is not fully representative of the

regional distribution of such farms in the nation. This does not affect the comparison of mechanized farms with non-mechanized ones within a region (the main use made of these data in this book), and it has little bearing on many of the generalizations derived from the survey. It does, however, affect the average for all sample farms wherever the characteristics that are averaged differ significantly between regions.

The shortcomings of both the Village Study and the Mechanization Study were, of course, borne in mind in using these data, and wherever necessary adjustments were made to compensate for biases, or the limitations clearly indicated where such adjustments could not be made.

III. Some Terms Used

A. Area Units and Equivalents

The area units used in Turkey and in this study are the decare and hectare, where 1 hectare = 10 decares. The approximate equivalents in acres are:

$$1 \text{ acre} = 4 \text{ decares}$$
$$2.47 \text{ acres} = 1 \text{ hectare}$$

B. Value of Turkish Money

The value of the Turkish lira during the years to which the estimates in this study refer (1951-1953) stood officially at TL. 2.8 = $1.00. On the free market $1.00 was equal to TL. 3.85 in 1951, TL. 4.89 in 1952, and TL. 5.59 in 1953.[34] Each lira contains 100 kuruş.

C. Regional Subdivisions

For administrative purposes Turkey was divided into sixty-three provinces during the years to which this study refers. In presenting

their results the Agricultural Division of the
Central Statistical Office generally tabulates
the statistics by provinces and also by regions,
nine in number, which have been marked out for
this purpose.[35] Central Anatolia, the heart of
the country, has been designated regions I, VIII
and IX, the Aegean area as II, the Marmara (which
includes European Thrace) III, the Mediterranean
in the south IV, the Black Sea area in the north
VII, and the mountainous eastern areas as regions
V and VI, the former being the northern portion
and the latter the southern one. For some purposes, as will be seen, it was more convenient
to work with regional tabulations, for others
the finer breakdowns by provinces proved to be
more useful.

PART I.

FUNCTIONAL DISTRIBUTION
OF INCOME

The object of this part of the study is to examine how agricultural income in Turkey is distributed functionally, i.e., what part of the net total is earned by land, labor, and capital. Before going on to derive this estimate, two problems must be pointed out since these problems determine the kind of estimates that must be made as well as the order of dealing with them.

1. Since animals are pastured on common land,[1] and any villager can use the land belonging to his village without paying rent for its use, no private rent should accrue to pasture land. Moreover, since no apparent limits are set on the number of animals that any villager can pasture on the land belonging to his village, pasture land should be treated as a free good and no rent be assigned to it, not even imputed rent.[2] On the other hand, in estimating the distribution of income from privately owned crop land, a return for rent very definitely has to be included. Because of this important difference in the ownership pattern between pasture land and crop land, it is more convenient to estimate separately the distribution of factor incomes derived from crops and animals.

2. As noted in the Introduction, crop land is typically owned by a peasant proprietor who also owns his equipment and works his farm with the help of his family. Since in most cases the family owns all the factors of production that contribute to the crop income it derives from the farm, one faces the problem of how to divide this imputed income functionally. The way this situation is sometimes dealt with is to treat mixed incomes separately, and to estimate the shares only for the sector of the economy where different factor incomes actually accrue to different persons. But for Turkey's agricultural sector this procedure would not lead to any meaningful results since the greater part of all incomes would then fall into the category of mixed incomes. The alternative is to attribute to each factor of production the income that

it could earn if it were hired. This is the
method that has been followed. But in so doing
another problem was encountered. In Turkey, as
in other countries in which the market system has
not permeated very far into the agricultural sector, the market system exists side by side with
a more traditional system of payment--the shares
system--so that the amount of income a factor
could earn if it were hired can differ, depending
on which system of payment it is assumed determines its imputed income. Thus in some instances
land is let out for a definite amount of money,
as in the market system, in others the rent consists of a share of the produce which the landlord divides with the tenant in certain prear-
ranged proportions. This is the shares system.
Which return should be chosen as the opportunity
cost of the land? What has been done is to consider both systems of payment, i.e., values for
their contribution were attributed to the factors
of production that earn imputed incomes, first
on the assumption that the market system prevails,
then on the assumption that the shares system
prevails. A comparison of the two sets of results, as will be shown, raises some extremely
interesting questions.

These problems have determined the kind
of preliminary estimates that had to be made before the over-all estimate of functional distribution in Turkish agriculture could be derived,
as well as the order in which these estimates
could be made. Since crop land is privately
owned and can be rented for money or a share of
the crop, there are two systems by which the imputed incomes of factors of production engaged
in crop production can be valued. However no
such separate systems of valuation apply to the
imputed income from animal products, since farmers do not pay for the use of the common land on
which the livestock is pastured, so that only
one estimate can be made in this instance. Because of these differences in the customs of land
use and valuation it is necessary to make separ-

ate estimates for the functional distributions of crop and animal incomes. The two distributions of the crop product are derived first, according to the market system in Chapter II,[3] and according to the shares system in Chapter III, and then the significance of the difference in the two types of results is examined in Chapter IV. Finally in Chapter V the functional distribution of animal incomes is derived and combined with the previous estimates to obtain the over-all distribution of functional incomes from crops and animals.

CHAPTER II

FUNCTIONAL DISTRIBUTION OF CROP INCOMES
ACCORDING TO THE MARKET SYSTEM

To derive a functional distribution of crop incomes statistically involves estimating how this
income is distributed among the factors of production. Before beginning to make this estimate
one must, however, decide on the number of factors of production whose share of income is to
be isolated, both because of the conceptual questions which this decision involves, as well as
the practical problems of estimation that it entails.

I. The Factors of Production

The classical economists conceived of
three factors of production: land, labor, and
capital.[1] The neoclassical economists added a
fourth factor, enterprise.[2] The question arises
as to which of the two conceptions should be
adopted for present purposes. If the return to
enterprise is conceived as a "windfall" that
accrues to enterprisers because conditions of
uncertainty are in their favor (or conversely,
losses accrue as a result of conditions of uncertainty working against them), then the neoclassical and classical conceptions would be the
same if windfalls were zero (or the conditions
of uncertainty were neutral).[3] But if they are
not zero the neoclassical conception is superior
because: (1) The categories are more homogeneous.
Windfalls, which are a distinct type of return,
are singled out. (2) One would expect that
windfalls would be much affected by random factors, particularly changes in crop size from year
to year in agriculture and price changes. As a
proportion of the total income they could thus

be expected to vary appreciably from one year to the next. If one's interest is in basic long-run relationships, as it is in this study, it would be well to isolate the windfall portion of total income in order to derive more representative and stable values for the other three returns.

Unfortunately, there is no way to estimate statistically the size of windfalls for any period. As will be seen, all that can be done with the available data is to derive the return to the landlord, valued according to the market system, as a residual income, thereby attributing to him a composite return which includes both rent and windfall. This procedure is logical for imputed incomes of owner-operators, but when the land is rented out the windfall would accrue to the tenant. Since in making the estimates in this chapter the windfall will be attributed entirely to rents--which is not always correct--while the purpose of these estimates is to derive long run values (without windfalls), in the end an attempt will be made to gauge to what extent the share that was estimated for rents is too large or too small because the crop in 1951 was greater or smaller than during a "normal" year.

Before beginning to estimate how crop incomes are distributed according to the market system it is necessary to derive a preliminary estimate of the total income that is to be divided between the factors. This total is needed because the incomes of each of the factors of production, estimated according to the market system in this chapter, must be expressed in a form comparable to the estimates made in Chapter III of income distribution according to the share system if the results of these two systems are to be compared.[4]

II. Size of the Net Crop Income

The national income originating in crop production was derived by using the estimate of the gross crop product less crop costs in the Turkish national income accounts as a point of departure.[5] This estimate required some adjustment because expenditures for work animals were not treated as a crop cost in obtaining this figure; instead animal costs were charged against the value of the animal output. But for present purposes expenditures for work animals must be considered a cost of crops, just as are expenditures for power-driven machinery, whose function is the same as that of work animals. After deducting these costs from the estimate in the national income accounts,[6] the national income originating in crop production, net of all non-factor costs, was found to amount to TL. 3,257 million in 1951, or 74.5 percent of the gross crop product.[7] This amount should represent the "value added" by crops during that year, and be equal to the sum of the factor incomes earned in crop production. It is this amount which, in the estimates that follow, will be divided among the factors.[8]

III. Wages

In Turkish agriculture most wages, including a good part of paid wages, are earned by farm operators. As noted in Chapter I, most of the work done on farms in Turkey is done by farm operators and their families working on their own farms. Only one out of nine village families are permanent agricultural workers.[9] But landless peasants are not the only ones who do farm work for wages. Farmers with insufficient incomes from farms they own or rent seek to supplement their incomes by temporarily sending away members of their families to earn wages elsewhere, and the number of these temporary workers is greater than the number of permanent ones.[10] A part of these temporary migrants look for work in towns;[11] a considerably larger number look for seasonal agricultural work for about six weeks[12] by temporarily migrating to other areas where the active agricultural season comes earlier or later than the period of activity on their own farms. During the harvest season few hands can be spared. But there are many months of slack during the rest of the year. This seasonal migration is helped by the great diversity of climate and crops in Turkey which varies the timing of harvest seasons. For example, in Central and Eastern Anatolia cereals, the main crop, are harvested in July and August, but cotton picking in the Mediterranean begins as early as April, stretching out into June, so that Central Anatolians can earn extra income picking cotton in the Mediterranean and return home in time for their own harvest.

To derive the total return to labor, one must therefore estimate both wages paid to hired labor and the value contributed by owner-operators to their own operations. Paid wages will be considered first.

A. <u>Paid Wages</u>

Paid agricultural wages are earned (1) by the permanent agricultural workers, and (2) by farm operators or members of their families for seasonal work done on ther people's farms.

(1) <u>Paid wages of permanent agricultural workers</u>. Total wages earned by permanent agricultural workers in 1951, the year to which the estimates of factor incomes refer, were derived by estimating (a) the number of such workers in 1951, and (b) the 1951 wage rates for permanent work.

(a) <u>Number of permanent agricultural workers</u>
The number of permanent agricultural workers in 1951 was found by interpolating the

numbers shown in the 1950 Agricultural Census
Results and the 1955 Census of Population, since
data for 1951 are not available.[13] The interpolated result raises two questions. First,
while the data for 1950 definitely refer to permanent agricultural workers, it is not clear whether those for 1955 do not also include seasonal
workers. However it is likely that primarily
permanent workers are included. The data in the
1955 Census of Population seem to refer to oc-
cupations during the week preceeding the census,
which was taken at the end of October when harvest work, the main employment of most seasonal
workers, is over, so that the 1950 and 1955 data
should be fairly homogeneous with respect to
types of workers included. The data raise still
another question. The 1955 figure is smaller
than that for 1950, when on grounds of population
increase one would have expected an increase.[14]
This rather unexpected result can probably be explained by the great influx of peasants into
cities between 1950 and 1955. (An increased number of peasants looking for permanent jobs seem
to have sought work in cities rather than on
farms.)[15] Therefore the figure of 310,000 (interpolated between the 1950 and 1955 figures)
will be accepted as the number of permanent agricultural workers in cities and villages in 1951.[16]

(b) Wages per worker

A 1948 estimate by the Director of Agriculture in Gaziantep Province put the yearly
wages of permanent hired workers at TL. 744.[17]
Adjusted for 1951 prices the figure becomes
TL. 753.[18] This agrees remarkably well with the
figure in the Village Study. If one adds the income in kind which was omitted in the study for
lack of data, and adjusts the prices of some
industrial goods paid in kind to make the data
apply to 1951, total yearly wages in the Village
Study at 1951 prices were TL. 763.[19] This figure was used as the average wage of permanent
agricultural workers. For 310,000 workers total
wages then amounted to TL. 237 million.

(2) Paid wages of seasonal workers

(a) Number of man-days worked

The 1949 Village Census provides figures
on the total number of seasonal wage workers and
the number of man-days worked.[20] These figures
are needed for 1951, however, and there is a
question whether these numbers had not increased
in the interim. On the one hand the agricultural population grew by about 4 percent;[21] on the
other hand, as noted earlier, there was an increased tendency of workers to look for work in
cities rather than in agriculture. There was
still a third factor. Tractors, while displac-
ing sharecroppers[22]--and there was a great increase
in the use of tractors between the two dates--
at the same time increased the need for seasonal
workers. On balance it seems likely that some
increase took place, though the precise figure
cannot be determined. The best estimate that
can be made is to assume that the rate of increase
was equal to the increase in the agricultural
population. This gives a total of 21,547,000 man-
days worked by seasonal agricultural workers in
1951. It should be noted that this figure excludes any seasonal wage work done by peasants
within their own villages, for which no data are
available. The actual total, therefore, should
be larger.

(b) Seasonal wage rates

The Village Study[23] shows monthly wages
to be TL. 138 (including the equivalent of food
paid in kind, but omitting the value of housing
provided, which is likely to be negligible for
seasonal workers), a rate which is over twice
that of permanent agricultural workers.[24] But
as harvest work is considerably harder and also
because the need for labor is greater at that
time, such a relationship between yearly and
seasonal wages is not unreasonable.[25] If the
same relationship is taken to hold between sea-

sonal and yearly wages in 1951, one derives a monthly wage of TL. 135, i.e., almost the same as the 1953 monthly wage in the Village Study. The corresponding daily wage, (of TL. 4.52) obtained as a proportion of the monthly wage, was then applied to the 21,547,000 man-days derived in the previous section giving a figure of TL. 97,392,000 for total wages of seasonal workers.

(c) Total paid wages

According to the calculations made above, total paid wages in 1951 were TL. 237 million for permanent workers and TL. 97 million for seasonal workers, or a total of TL. 334 million.

B. Imputed Wages

The imputed wages of farm operators who work on their own farms can be figured in different ways depending on the opportunity cost attributed to their work.

(1) Assuming that the value of labor is equal to the yearly wage of permanent agricultural workers. In this method every male between eighteen and sixty-four years of age who is engaged in agricultural work is assigned the wage earned by permanent agricultural workers. In doing so it is assumed that as permanent workers they would live on the landlord's land with their wives and young children, so that no separate wages would be assigned to the women, and that once a young man becomes eighteen, he can hire himself out as a permanent worker on his own account. Yearly wages calculated this way total TL. 2,410 million.[26]

(2) Assuming that the value of labor is equal to the wages of seasonal labor for forty-five days. The previous estimate was based on the assumption that the opportunity cost of the labor of self-employed peasants is equal to the

yearly wage of hired workers. Theory suggests
that if the value of the marginal product of
this labor were used instead of the wage, the
same figure would be derived since the wage is
taken to equal the marginal product under com-
petition. The evidence suggests, however, that
the assumptions are not borne out in Turkish
agriculture among peasant proprietors. Observations on unemployment make this evident. Thus
Christiansen-Weniger estimates that on a farm of
five hectares in Central Anatolia (i.e., a farm
considerably above average size in Turkey), with
two oxen, only 161 man-days of work are required,
plus the help of women and children during the
harvest season.[27] Similarly, Paul Stirling shows
that in the village in Central Anatolia where he
lived the busy period for men consisted of only
five to six months.[28] Some observers, in fact,
have gone so far as to question whether there is
not a permanent excess of labor. For example, in
an official report disguised unemployment is estimated to have been 48 percent of the agricultural population.[29]

      If this latter estimate is taken as being
valid one would have to conclude that the marginal
product of labor in agriculture is zero because
the marginal worker, if employed, would not add
to output. Some workers earn wages when they
hire themselves out, as has been seen, but this
does not disprove the proposition that the marginal product of the peasant proprietor may be
zero. The marginal product of labor which is
hired out could be equal to its wage, but the
marginal product of self-employed labor could be
zero. If this were so, one would expect that
there would be great pressure on the labor market tending to push wages down. Yet wages might
not fall anywhere near even a conventional subsistence level since working one's own land con-
veys social prestige. Thus it is conceivable
that, even if a small proprietor could derive no
more income from his operations, including rent
and return on investment as well as imputed

wages, than he could from working as a laborer
for someone else, he would still prefer to cultivate his own land. There is some evidence, in
fact, that this seems to be the case.[30]

But there is reason to doubt that the
marginal productivity of peasant proprietors is
zero. Marginal productivity of agricultural
labor should properly be calculated on a <u>yearly</u>
rather than a daily or monthly basis. When there
is a surplus of labor in industry it is likely
to exist with little regard for the time of the
year. But in agriculture the surplus may exist
only during certain seasons while during other
seasons there may actually be a shortage of manpower. The marginal product of labor should not
be thought of as the value of the product added
on the last day, but the value added by the last
man during the season. This value may change
from day to day or from season to season, and
the average yearly marginal product would not
be zero unless it is zero during all days of the
year.

The evidence suggests that in Turkey the
marginal product of labor is not zero during the
whole year. Thus, during World War II, the trend
of agricultural output which had been increasing
up to that time reversed itself, to pick up again
after the war.[31] The drafting of men into the
armed forces seemed to have reduced agricultural
output. And there is evidence of a shortage of
labor during the harvest season generally. Thus
Paul Stirling, who shows that the men are busy
during five to six months of the year, refers to
the harvest season as a period of feverish activity for everyone[32] and John Morrison points
out that during the harvest even the shepherds
have to return to the villages because all hands
are needed.[33] At harvest time Istanbul period-
ically experiences a shortage of unskilled labor
as peasants who come to work in town return to
their villages to help with the harvest.[34] The
relatively high wage rates for seasonal labor

calculated above (which were over twice as high
as yearly wages calculated on a per day basis),
give further evidence of the fact that there is
no surplus of labor during the harvest period.

In sum, there is excess labor only in
the seasonal sense. But even though the marginal
product of labor is not zero, the marginal product of the self-employed laborer must be lower
than that of permanently hired labor since underemployment exists among small proprietors. Thus,
an intermediate figure must be estimated. The
marginal product can be estimated by observing
that the marginal product of peasant proprietors
must be above zero at least for the period of
the harvest season, which lasts about forty-five
days; since there is a shortage of labor during
that period, the marginal product of peasant
proprietors at that time should not be less than
the wage paid to harvest labor during this season. The total earnings of labor were thus estimated as follows: From the number of males and
females fifteen to sixty-four years old engaged
in agriculture in 1951,[35] the number of permanent
agricultural workers (for whom paid wages have
already been calculated above) was deducted,
since no imputed wages should be assigned to them
in addition. To the males the same seasonal wage
of TL. 4.52 was assigned as that used earlier to
calculate paid seasonal wages, which is assumed
to represent the value of the marginal product
of self-employed labor per day--and to the women
two thirds of this wage[36]--and the harvest period
was taken to last forty-five days,[37] yielding
total imputed harvest wages of TL. 1,243 million.[38]

C. The Proportion of Wages in the Total Product
    According to the Various Estimates

The estimates of total wages that have
been derived are thus the following:
1. Adding together paid wages of TL. 334

million and the estimate of imputed wages derived
in (a) above--on the assumption that the marginal
product of self-employed labor can be measured
by the return to labor hired on a yearly basis--
of TL. 2,410 million, a figure of TL. 2,744 million is derived. Since the total net product was
estimated to have amounted to TL. 3,257 million
(see p.22 above), according to the first estimate
wages would amount to 84 percent of the total
product.

2. Adding together paid wages of TL. 334
million and the estimate of imputed wages derived
in (b) above--on the assumption that the marginal
product of self-employed labor can be measured
by wages of forty-five days harvest labor--of
TL. 1,243 million, a figure of TL. 1,577 million
is derived. This accounts for 48 percent of the
total net product.

It seems very likely that the first figure is too high, but that the second is too low.
The second figure should rather be taken as the
minimum value of the marginal product of labor.

IV. Return on Investment

The return to capital used in crop production constitutes the most difficult and pre-
carious part of the estimates of the functional
distribution according to the market system.
The reason is twofold: First, the statistics on
the value of total investments are very incom-
plete and, even where they are available, in
many cases they are subject to a relatively large
margin of error. Second, there is the problem
of determining the appropriate rate of return on
these investments.

The capital used for crop production takes
many forms. It includes tools and equipment,
such as plows, threshers, carts, and the like,
as well as tractors and other mechanical equipment. In addition there are investments in build-

ings used for production, primarily for storage
of crops and equipment. Work animals, too,
should be considered an investment made for crop
production, as should the stalls needed to house
them.

For the investments listed above data are
available to estimate their value, though they
are of varying quality. But the total value of
capital should also include the value of trees
that yield crops only after a gestation period
of one or more years, and of land improvements
made, such as irrigation works, wells, levelling
of ground, and any other improvements made in
the landscape that help to increase the production or distribution of crops. For the latter
types of investment the data are little more
than impressions, or else completely unavail-
able. The result of this gap is that the total
value of capital that will be derived in this
chapter will fall short of the actual total,
possibly by a considerable amount.

In spite of these difficulties, an attempt will be made to estimate the return to
capital for those investments for which data
are available, and the findings will be quali-
fied later. These investments will be treated
under the following headings: (A) tractors and
modern equipment, (B) work animals, (C) buildings,
and (D) simple tools and equipment.

A. Return from Investments in Tractors and Other
Modern Equipment

The method used for calculating the total
income derived from investments in tractors and
other modern equipment used in crop production
consists of estimating the rate of return derived
from this equipment by the farmers in the
Mechanization Study, and then applying this rate
to the estimated total value of such equipment in
the nation in 1951, the year for which the estimates of factor incomes are made.

(1) <u>The rate of return in the Mechanization Study</u>. For the farmers in the Mechanization Study the net income derived from the use of
tractors and other equipment is estimated by figuring the increase in their gross income due to
the use of modern equipment and by subtracting
from this the costs of this equipment. The factors that contributed to increase gross incomes
and that are included in these calculations are
(1) increased yields that can be ascribed to
tractors and other modern equipment, (2) income
earned by mechanized farmers by working land
with tractors for others for pay, and (3) savings
in the cost of labor and draft animals. The
equipment costs consist of (1) depreciation of
machinery and equipment, (2) costs of repairs
and spare parts, and (3) fuel costs. The resulting net returns are then taken as a percent of
the value of the investment in the equipment from
which they are derived, minus depreciation, to
obtain the rate of return. This rate was found
to be 56 percent.[39] Details on the methods used
to derive the results are explained in Appendix B.

(2) <u>The total value of modern agricultural equipment used in the nation in 1951, and
the total income derived from this investment.</u>
There are no data on the total value of modern
agricultural equipment in the country. However
data are available for the total number of tractors in the country in 1951, and one can also
calculate from the Mechanization Study that the
investment in tractors consisted of 74.6 percent
of the total investment in modern equipment.[40]
Assuming that on the average in the nation a new
tractor is worth as much as the average value of
a new tractor in the Mechanization Study, and
assuming, too, that mechanized farmers generally
own as much supplementary equipment as do the
farmers in the Mechanization Study, the total
investment in modern equipment in the country in
1951 could be calculated from these data. The
number of tractors in Turkey in 1951[41] was multi-

plied by the new value per tractor calculated from
the Mechanization Study and the same proportion
was added to this total for accompanying equipment for the nation as the proportion reported by
the farmers in the Mechanization Study.[42] From
this the estimated depreciation to 1951 was deducted by taking account of the age of tractors in
Turkey at the time[43] and by assuming that the
other equipment is of the same age as the tractors.[44]
This gave a present value of the total investment
in tractors and modern equipment of TL. 250 million in 1951.[45] Applying the rate of return of 56
percent to this investment, a total return from
all modern agricultural equipment of TL. 140 million was derived.

B. Income from Investments in Work Animals

The value of the stock of work animals
can be estimated from data on the number of animals and their prices. The number of each type
of work animal in villages is given for 1950 in
the 1950 Agricultural Census Results,[46] and 1951
prices for each type of animal have been obtained
from the Central Statistical Office. These
prices were reduced by 20 percent because, according to the detailed national income data for
Turkey, the prices of the Central Statistical
Office are gathered in provincial centers and
would be about 20 percent lower at the farm.[47]
From these data a total value of work animals in
1950 at 1951 prices after the 20 percent reduction was calculated. In 1951 the number of work
animals should not have been appreciably larger.[48]
To this investment was added the value of buildings used for work animals, yielding a total investment of TL. 1,059 million.[49]
No basis exists for determining a very
precise figure for the rate of return from work
animals. The typical (median) farmer in Turkey
has only two oxen,[50] the minimum necessary for
cultivating his land. Without them his crop income would be zero. Yet one cannot therefore

attribute the whole of the crop income as the marginal product of work animals. Since most farmers are able to invest in non-work animals, and the best estimate of the rate of return on this investment is that shown in Appendix C of roughly 34 percent including some imputed rent on pasture land,[51] this might be taken as the opportunity cost of investing in work animals. It can be argued that this figure is too low because farmers would first invest in work animals, and invest in non-work animals only whatever surplus savings are left over. On the other hand, plowing their own land is a way of life to peasant proprietors and for that they must purchase work animals before investing in other livestock, even if the marginal product of the draft beast were to be lower than the return on non-work animals. While the figure of 34 percent is hardly ideal, it is used because it is the best one available.

The total return on work animals, then, at a rate of return of 34 percent, is TL. 360 million.

C. Return on Investments in Non-Animal Buildings and Simple Tools and Equipment

The return on non-animal buildings and simple tools and equipment was derived from the Central Statistical Office estimate of the value of all agricultural equipment, including small tools as well as machinery for 1951.[52] From this estimate one can obtain the separate value of simple tools by subtracting the value of tractors and modern equipment estimated earlier in this chapter.[53] To the residual value for simple tools and equipment must be added the value of non-animal buildings, estimated at TL. 112 million,[54] giving a total investment of TL. 499 million for small tools, non-mechanical equipment, and non-animal buildings.

The remaining problem is to assign a rate of return on this investment. Since the portion

of the rate of 34 percent estimated for animals
in the Village Study that should be attributed
to imputed rent on pasture land is not known, to
be on the conservative side a rate of 20 percent
was used. The result is a total return from investment in simple tools and equipment and in
non-animal buildings of TL. 100 million.

D. The Total Return of Capital

        It was calculated above that the total
return to capital was TL. 600 million, of which
TL. 140 million is the return on investment in
tractors and modern equipment, TL. 360 million
the return from work animals, and TL. 100 million derived from small tools and non-animal
buildings. Together these investment returns
constitute 18 percent of the net crop income.
For reasons already indicated, the estimates are
exceedingly rough for work animals and small
tools, particularly the latter. This figure of
TL. 600 million does not include the total return to capital since, as noted above, the statistics on agricultural investments are not all-
inclusive. There are many small improvements
made on farms that are exceedingly difficult if
not impossible to measure, the value of which
taken together may by no means be negligible. If
these could be included in the total, the return
to investment would be larger. Such investment
is ordinarily not distinguished from the value
of the land so that the return from it is counted
as part of the landlord's income. This means
that the income from the land also includes some
return to capital. On the other hand, as was
pointed out above,[55] the return on investment
also includes some imputed rent on pasture land,
and to some extent at least these over-and understatements cancel out. To what extent they do
cannot, however, be determined.

V. Rents

According to Ricardian theory, if market forces are allowed to work out their effect, rents are the residual after all factor incomes have received their market values or, according to marginal productivity theory, the value of their marginal products.[56] Assuming that the estimates of the proportion of wages of 48 percent and of the return to capital of 18 percent derived above represent the value of the marginal products of these factors, the residual left for rent would be 33 percent. It should be noted, however, that the 48 percent figure for wages is a minimum estimate, and to the extent to which actual wage incomes are larger, the proportion of rent in the total income would be smaller. It should be noted, too, that the residual income includes some return on investment, as well as windfalls,[57] while on the other hand, some rent is included in the return to capital.

Table 1 (see p. 37) summarizes the results of the estimates made in this chapter. They are called preliminary because there is reason to believe, as indicated in note 4 to Chapter II, that the value of the crop output used for these computations (which is based on official figures), is too large. Revising this value downward changes the proportions, as will be seen in Chapter IV, where this adjustment is made and the final estimate is derived.[58]

TABLE 1

SUMMARY OF PRELIMINARY ESTIMATE OF FACTOR INCOMES
ACCORDING TO MARKET VALUATIONS IN 1951

		In millions of TL.	As % in the net crop product
		(1)	(2)
A.	Wages		
	1. Paid wages		
	- of permanent agricultural workers	(237)[a]	
	- of seasonal agricultural workers	(97)[b]	
	2. Imputed wages (for 45 days harvest work)	(1,243)[c]	
	TOTAL WAGES	1,577	48%
B.	Return to capital		
	1. For work animals and their buildings	(360)[d]	
	2. For tools, non-mechanical equipment and buildings other than those used for work animals	(100)[e]	
	3. For tractors and other modern equipment	(140)[f]	
	TOTAL RETURN TO CAPITAL	600	18%
C.	Rent (the residual income)		
	TOTAL RENT	1,080[g]	33%
D.	Total national income originating in crop production		
		3,257[h]	100%[i]

Sources: See text and footnotes in this chapter.

a. The number of permanent agricultural workers is estimated to be 310,000, and their average yearly wage TL. 763. See pp. 23-24 for sources and methods of derivation.

b. Based on a daily wage of TL. 4.52 for 21,547,000 man-days. See p.25.

c. Estimated for self-employed farm operators between the ages of 15 and 65 for 45 days, by assuming that the value of men's work per day, for the 3,266,000 men, is equal to the daily wage of TL. 4.52 earned by hired labor at harvest time, and that the contribution of the 4,276,000 women is worth 2/3 as much as that of men. For details and assumptions see pp.26-29.

d. Derived by attributing to the estimated value of investment in work animals and their buildings of TL. 1,059 million a rate of return of 34%. See pp. 33-34.

e. The value of this investment is estimated at TL. 387 million for simple tools and non-mechanical equipment, plus TL. 112 million for non-animal buildings. The rate of return on this investment is assumed to be 20%. See pp. 34-35.

f. Based on a rate of 56% on a total investment of TL. 250 million for this type of equipment. See pp. 31-33.

g. This is calculated as the residual after deducting all other factor incomes from the estimated actual national income originating in crop production in 1951. See p. 36.

h. Estimated on p. 22.

i. Percentages do not add up due to rounding.

CHAPTER III

FUNCTIONAL DISTRIBUTION OF CROP INCOMES ACCORDING TO THE SHARE SYSTEM

In Chapter II the functional distribution of the crop product was derived according to the market system. In this chapter it will be estimated according to the share system. Rent shares will be considered first because somewhat more data are available for rents than for the separate shares of labor and capital.

I. Rent Shares

The estimate of rents is made in two parts: (1) The proportion that rents absorb of the total crop product under different conditions is established and (2) these findings are used to estimate the average share that rents take of the total crop product.

A. The Proportion of Rents in the Gross or Net Crop Product under Different Conditions

Very few data are available on the proportion of the gross or net crop product paid in rent shares, but the few data there are roughly seem to agree. One source, Evans Fotos, "Land Tenure and Rural Organization in Turkey Since 1923"[1] reports that the tenant gets 50 percent of the crop if he cultivates low-income crops such as cereals, or if the land is located in areas where manpower is needed to cultivate fields that would otherwise be idle. But the peasant gets a smaller share of the crop in regions where there is greater population pressure, or where the crop gives a high return per decare, as with

cotton, tobacco, grapes and nuts. For these
crops the tenant's share is one fourth to one
third of the crop.[2]

Fotos does not make it clear whether in
the fifty-fifty system the landlord shares in
the expenses but in some passages he seems indirectly to show that he does. He mentions that
grapes leave the peasant with a smaller share
than cereals and gives as an example share-crop-
ping arrangements in the Aegean vineyard region
where the peasant keeps one half to two thirds
of the (gross) crop if he bears all expenses (so
that the landlord would get a clear return of
one half to one third of the gross crop output
as rent), while if the landlord bears all operating expenses, the peasant gets one third to one
half of the net output after all expenses are
deducted from the crop.[3] As the rents from cereal land are said to be smaller, one can infer
from this that the landlord's share of cereals
is less than one half to one third of the gross
crop output, or, in other words, that the landlord shares in the costs.

Fotos' general findings are supported
by Richard D. Robinson, although Robinson is more
definite about costs. Robinson reports that according to his observations the fifty-fifty system is the most frequently practiced arrangement
in Gaziantep province, and thinks that it may
possibly be the most common one in Turkey. In
this system the landlord gives the land and seed.[4]
In another place he makes it clear that the
fifty-fifty system traditionally means that the
cropper and the owner share certain costs of
production, after which the crop is divided
fifty-fifty.[5]

Robinson also shows that rents have increased with the introduction of tractors and
the extension of cotton cultivation in some
southern regions. He refers here to areas where
population pressure is great and where absentee
land ownership is common. In such regions
sharecropping has mostly given way to a system

of hired labor. But for the sharecropping arrangements that remain, the fifty-fifty system was changed from one where landlord and tenant share the costs, to one where all costs are borne by the tenant[6] (so that the landlord would get 50 percent of the gross crop output).

The third source of data on rents is the Village Study. Here the data refer to an area with less population pressure than in many coastal regions, and an area where cereals primarily are grown.[7] In the Village Study rents also appear to conform to some kind of fifty-fifty system. Although rents are listed in money and not as a share, the data make it clear that over 90 percent of the rental payments are made in kind, and that the larger part of the money value of rents listed in the study represents the cash equivalent of rents paid in produce. In Table 1 (see p.42) it is shown that one approximates a fifty-fifty share system of the net product, at least for the three lowest land brackets, if the net product is taken to be equal to the gross product minus twice the value of the seed, i.e., if the cost of seed is considered to be one half the cost of production. The idea of calculating rents this way derives from Robinson's observation that the landlord shares in the costs of production by providing the seed, and the data in the Village Study show that seeds would indeed constitute half the total (non-factor) cost.[8]

It should be noted that no mention is made in the Village Study of the owner paying any share of the expenses. This should not be taken as evidence, however, that the landlord does not pay. It is possible that among the particular group sampled in the Village Study the practice prevalent in Central Anatolia was not followed, but it seems far more likely that the farmers in question were not asked about the contribution made by the land owner to meet expenses and as a result this information was merely omitted.

TABLE 1

RENTS IN THE VILLAGE STUDY

	Farms by land-size brackets (in decares)			
	10-79	80-159	160-499	500 and over
	(1)	(2)	(3)	(4)
Rent as percent of net income[a]	53.3%	58.0%	59.9%	112.2%
Rent as percent of gross income from which cost of seed is deducted twice[b]	49.2%	49.5%	47.3%	92.7%

a. Calculated from Village Study Table 33, and Appendix A, Table 2.

b. Calculated from Village Study, Table 2.

The rents of the farmers in the three lowest land brackets in the Village Study thus seem to conform to a fifty-fifty system of the net product if costs are defined as above. But the rents of the farmers in the largest land bracket certainly do not seem to. Thus Table 1 shows that as a percent of the net product, calculated by deducting from the gross product either the actual costs of the large farmers, or twice the cost of seed, rents are close to, or even over, 100 percent.

One wonders why the rents of the large farmers should be so much higher than those of the farmers in the other land brackets, and why for these farmers renting land actually seems unprofitable. One possible explanation is that only a part of the costs of these farmers should be assigned to the newly rented land. For if these farmers rented additional land after they bought tractors,[9] because the tractors could cultivate a larger area than these farmers had operated before, then the operation of additional land would be profitable so long as the rent is lower than the net marginal product of operating a larger land area. There is a good likelihood that this is what has actually happened. The Mechanization Study shows that when farmers bought tractors they typically expanded the area of their operations by first taking over themselves land which they owned but had previously rented out, and subsequently by buying and renting additional land.[10]

This would explain why it may have been profitable for the large farmers in the Village Study to pay such high rents, but still leaves open the question how rents of large farmers could be so much higher than those of others, i.e., why they should have to pay them. Would not the greater ability to pay high rents on the part of large farmers raise rents all around? And even if large farmers rented their land more recently than other farmers, since rental arrangements in Turkey seem to be made for only short periods of time,[11] one would expect that at least some of this increase be reflected in the rents of other farmers. But the data in Table 1 do not show this to be the case. One is thus still left with the question why there should be two systems of rent, one for large farmers and one for smaller ones.

But closer analysis suggests that the large farmers actually pay the same proportion of the crop as rent as do the smaller ones. The reason the figures in Table 1 appear to lead to a different conclusion is that when the rents of large farmers are calculated as a proportion of the output of rented land alone, the ratio of rent to output should be lower than when rents per decare are calculated as a proportion of the output per decare of rented land and owned land, as was done in Table 1. Since it can be assumed with a good deal of confidence that the large farmers who rent land are mechanized and therefore should obtain yields that are considerably higher than those obtained by farmers who are not mechanized,[12] and since not all large farmers (i.e., those in the highest group) in the Village Study, are mechanized[13] the output per decare on rented land (presumably operated with tractors) should be higher than the average output per decare of all large farmers from both mechanized and unmechanized operations.

It is possible to estimate the value of output on rented land obtained by large farmers in the Village Study and these calculations show that the rent of these farmers bears about the same relationship to the value of output from rented land as for the other land brackets.[14] It appears therefore that the rents of large farmers are calculated in the same manner as the rents of farmers in other land brackets, a conclusion supported by the fact that 96 percent of the rents paid by large farmers are paid in produce,[15] so that they are most probably figured as a share of the crop.

Thus the three sources of data roughly confirm one another, although there are some variations. So far as rents of cereal land are concerned, according to Fotos they would be less than one third to one half of the gross output, although it is not clear how much they would be precisely. According to Robinson and the Village Study, cereal rents would be 50 percent of the gross output, minus the cost of seed,[16] which would make the net rents fall somewhere within the range of Fotos' figures. Seed costs, moreover, are taken to be roughly equal to one half of all non-factor crop costs. For better crops rents are one half of the gross crop product (with no deductions for costs) according to Robinson,[17] and between one third and one half of the gross output (with no deductions for costs) according to Fotos.[18]

B. Estimate of Actual Total Rent as a Proportion of the Gross and Net Crop Product

From the shares calculated so far it is possible to estimate roughly how much of the crop income in Turkey is earned in the form of rent. As rents differ for different types of crops the estimate is broken down according to types of crops.

(1) Cereal rents. The above analysis has shown that cereal rents are 50 percent of the gross product minus the cost of seed. In the national income estimates the cost of cereal seeds in 1951 amounted to TL. 371 million,[19] and the gross output of cereals to TL. 2,417 million.[20] This gives a total for cereal rents of TL. 837 million.

(2) Rents on higher income crops. Table 2 on page 51 below shows the gross income per decare of the major crops in 1952 and 1955, and suggests that besides tobacco, cotton,

grapes, and nuts, mentioned by Fotos as higher income crops subject to higher rents, sugar beet and "other industrial crops" should also be included in this class. To this list should be added tea, which is reputed to be a most profitable crop, although no data are available to calculate the income per decare which it yields. In 1951 the value of these higher income crops amounted to TL. 1,477 million.[21]

In determining the share of this crop income that would go to rent the problem arises that there are two sets of rent data for these better crops. According to Robinson these rents are 50 percent of the gross output, and according to Fotos 33-50 percent. It is possible, however, that Robinson's higher rents observed in cotton areas referred to a crop with a considerably higher income per decare than Fotos' rent data observed in vineyard regions. This is not readily apparent in Table 2 where the income per decare from cotton land is not very much higher than the income from grapes. But cotton prices in 1952 were just declining from spectacular increases in preceding years (the index of cotton prices, 1948 = 100, stood at 165, 155, and 137 during the years 1950, 1951, and 1952, respectively),[22] and cotton rents reported by Robinson in 1952 must therefore have been based on the very high recent incomes when cotton was clearly in the same category as other industrial crops whose income per decare is considerably higher than the income from gapes. Therefore it appears reasonable to assign Robinson's higher rate to the industrial crops and Fotos' lower one to grapes. This still leaves open the question as to what rents to assign to nuts and tea, the crops for which no data on income per decare are available. As tea is reputed to be a most profitable crop, it will be grouped with industrial crops, and nuts will be grouped with grapes so as not to overstate the total rents. This gives rents for industrial crops and tea of TL. 584 million, and for grapes and nuts of

TL. 129 million, or total imputed rents of
TL. 713 million for higher income crops.[23]

(3) Rents for other crops. In these
rent calculations rents on TL. 475 million, or
11 percent of the crop output, have been omitted
since cereals and the more lucrative crops combined accounted for only 89 percent of the total
crop output. The remaining crops are pulses,
olives, and fruits other than grapes, olives,
and nuts. Table 2 shows that the income per
decare from pulses and olives is relatively low,
but data are not available on the income per
decare from the other fruit. Therefore these
crops will be assigned the rents of cereal land
(50 percent of the gross output less the cost of
seed, or the equivalent), so as not to overstate
rents.[24] This gives additional rents of TL. 158
million.[25]

By adding up the imputed rents calculated
for these various crops a figure for total imputed rents of TL. 1,708 million is derived,
which is 39 percent of the gross crop output or
52 percent of the net national income originating
in crop production.[26]

II. The Shares of Labor and Capital

In most share arrangements the peasant
does the work and also brings his tools and work
animals, so that the share left to him after he
turns over a part of the crop to the landlord
includes a return for both his labor and capital.
This combined share can, of course, be derived
indirectly from the data on rents, since labor
and capital together get the remainder left over
after rents are paid. Rents were estimated
above to be 50 percent of the gross product and,
for cereals, also 50 percent of the net product,
because in this case the landlord and peasant
each pay half of the cost.[27] For more lucrative
crops the proportion is also 50 percent of the

gross product, but since the peasant bears all the costs, the shares as a percent of the net product are greater than 50 percent for the landlord and smaller for the peasant. The peasant's share in all these cases includes the return for both work and capital. It remains to determine the shares that go to wages and capital separately.

The data available for making such an estimate are very scanty. One source is Morrison's account of Alişar, a village in Central Anatolia where the main crop is wheat. Morrison mentions that the share of the agricultural worker in Alişar is one third to one fourth of the crop, the proportion being greater if he also contributes his tools and work animals.[28] The share of capital in Morrison's village can be derived indirectly from that of wages. Since rents are 50 percent of the gross product (before deductions for seed costs)[29] and wages 25-33 percent,[30] the residual left for capital is 25-17 percent (also before deductions of costs).

These incomes can be calculated as a proportion of the net product. According to the analysis in Section I of this chapter, the net shares vary for different crops depending on which of the factors of production pay for the costs. Thus it was seen that the cost of seed is borne by the landlord when he rents cereal land, and paid by the peasant when the land is used for better crops. It was also noted that in share arrangements seed costs are taken, on the average, as equal to one half the cost. Since crop costs in the national income data are estimated to be 25.5 percent of the gross crop product[31] and since twice the cost of seed in the Village Study amount to 26 percent[32] (i.e., about the same proportion), crop costs will be taken as equal to 26 percent of the gross output and seed costs as 13 percent. The other 13 percent of costs consist primarily of feed for work animals and other expenditures for draft power and tools, which would have to be ascribed

to capital, and some small expenditures for
sacks, baskets, etc., which are likely to come
out of the worker's share.[33] From the data in
the Village Study it can be estimated that, of
the non-seed costs of 13 percent, 11 percent are
costs incurred for maintenance and depreciation
of capital, and 2 percent costs to be deducted
from wages.[34] With these cost data one can calculate that the share of the net product that
labor receives falls within the range between 31
and 42 percent. Since, as has been seen, land
on which grain is grown yields a rent of 50 percent of the net product, between 19 and 8 percent is the remainder left for capital.[35]

        Morrison's figures refer only to land on
which cereals and pulses are grown, i.e., crops
that yield a relatively low return per decare.
On land used to grow a more lucrative crop, cotton, Robinson reports, as has been noted, that
the tenant and landlord each receive half the
crop (as with land on which grain is grown), but
that the sharecropper bears all of the cost, including the cost of seed. The question arises,
however, what proportion of this added cost is
borne by the one who supplies the labor and what
proportion by the one who supplies the capital
where capital and labor are contributed by different individuals. Unfortunately, no evidence
is available on this point and in its absence
the best guess is that capital and labor share
the added costs equally. The result derived on
this basis is that for better crops labor receives
between 22 and 32 percent of the net product and
capital between 10 and 0 percent.[36]

        The results of these calculations are sum-
marized in Table 3 (see page 52) which shows
the proportion of gross and net income received
by each of the factors for low-income and for
higher-income crops, as well as the proportions
received in the nation for all crops computed by
weighting the proportions of the two types. Unfortunately no data are available to reduce the

range of the estimates of wages and the return
to capital in the shares system.   In the absence
of any other data the estimates must be left in
this form; the best estimates that can be derived of the over-all functional distribution of
income in the shares system are the data for all
crops shown in Table 3, column 3, in this chapter.

TABLE 2

GROSS INCOME PER DECARE FROM MAJOR CROPS
IN 1952 AND 1955
(In TL.)[a]

	1952	1955
Cereals	31	30
Pulses	35	38
Olives	35	25
Grapes	62	82
Industrial crops		
- average, all crops	108	145
- tobacco	134	199
- cotton	82	90
- sugar beets	108	144
- "other" industrial crops	141	194

a. Calculated from Turkey, Agricultural Bank, Türkiye
Zirai İstihsal Kıymeti 1952 (Statistical Consultation
Service No. 1) and Turkey, Agricultural Bank, Türkiye
Zirai İstihsal Kıymeti 1955 (Statistical Consultation
Service No. 4), which give the total value of output
of the main crops and from the Monthly Bulletin of
Statistics, No. 34-36, in which the area planted to
these crops is shown.

TABLE 3

ESTIMATE OF FACTOR SHARES IN SHARE ARRANGEMENTS AS PERCENT
OF THE GROSS AND NET PRODUCTS WHEN LAND IS SOWN
TO LOW AND HIGHER INCOME CROPS AND TO ALL CROPS

		Gross shares as % of the gross product (before any cost deductions) (1)	Net shares as % of gross product (2)	Net shares as % of net product (3)
Low Income Crops				
1.	Rents	50 (a)	37 (b)	50 (c)
2.	Wages	25-33 (d)	23-31 (e)	31-42 (f)
3.	Capital	25-17 (g)	14- 6 (h)	19- 8 (i)
4.	Total	100% (j)	74% (k)	100% (l)
Higher Income Crops				
5.	Rents	50 (m)	50 (n)	68 (o)
6.	Wages	25-33 (p)	16-24 (q)	22-32 (r)
7.	Capital	25-17 (s)	8- 0 (t)	10- 0 (u)
8.	Total	100% (v)	74% (w)	100% (x)
All Crops (y)				
9.	Rents	50	39	52
10.	Wages	25-33	21-28	28-38
11.	Capital	25-17	14- 7	19- 9
12.	Total	100%	74%	100%[z]

a. See pp. 44-45.

b. Seed costs are taken to be 13% of the gross product or 1/2 of the total cost of 26%. In the case of cereal land seeds are supplied out of the landlord's share. (See pp. 48-49.)

c. The net product is taken to be 74% of the gross (see note (b) above). Therefore 37% of the gross product is 50% of the net.

d. Information supplied by Morrison, op. cit., p. 16.

e. Since the landlord supplies the seed for cereals, the only deductions to be made from gross wages are costs for baskets, etc., estimated to be 2% of the gross product. (See note 34 to this chapter.)

f. Calculated by same method as that shown in note (c) above. (See also note 35 to this chapter.)

g. Derived by subtraction. When rents are 50% and wages 25%, the share left to capital is 25%. When wages are 33% the share left to capital is 17%.

h. Assuming that costs other than seed costs are 13% of the gross product, and that 11% of this cost is attributable to capital. The other 2% was attributed to wages.

i. Derived by same method as shown in note (f). (See also note 35 to this chapter.)

j. The sum of the gross shares must, of course, equal 100% of the gross product.

k. The sum of the net shares is equal to 74% of the gross product because costs are taken to be 26% of the gross product.

l. The sum of the net shares is equal to 100% of the net product.

m. Gross crop shares are taken to be the same for higher income crops as for cereals (see pp. 39-40 and 45).
    The difference in rents between high and low income crops is affected only by the distribution of costs between landlord and tenant.

n. This figure is the same as in column (1), line (5) since seed costs for the higher income crops are borne by the peasant and no deductions are made from the share of the landlord in this case.

o. Derived by same method as shown in note (f).
    $(68\% = \dfrac{50\%}{74\%})$

p. See note (m) above.

q. For the higher income crops we have assumed that capital and labor share the seed costs. Therefore, the shares of 25-33% and 25-17% are reduced by $6\frac{1}{2}\%$ of the gross product each. In addition another 2% reduction is made for small costs likely borne by labor and 11% for costs borne by capital.

r. Same method used as explained in note (o) above. (See also note 36 to this chapter.)

s. See note (q) above.

t. See note (q) above.

u. See note (r) above.

v. See note (j) above.

w. See note (k) above.

x. See note (l) above.

y. Rent in column (3) was computed directly (see pp.46-47) and so was the proportion of costs to gross income of 26%. The other shares (for wages and capital) in columns (2) and (3) were computed as a weighted average of the residual incomes (after total rents had been deducted from the total incomes in columns (2) and (3).)

z. Percentages do not add to 100 due to rounding.

CHAPTER IV

FUNCTIONAL DISTRIBUTION OF CROP INCOMES
ACCORDING TO THE MARKET AND
THE SHARE SYSTEMS COMPARED

In Table 1 (see p. 56) the estimates of the distribution of crop incomes when distributed according to the shares and the market systems are summarized. The table shows that the two estimates of factor incomes do not support one another. For the return to capital the difference is small. The share of capital in the market system is 18 percent, falling within the range of 9 - 19 percent estimated for the share system.

But the difference is quite large for rents and wages. The estimate for rents, according to the share system is 52 percent of the net product, but only 33 percent when estimated as a residual in the market system or a difference of 19 percentage points. For labor the difference is between 10 and 20 percentage points since wages in the shares system receive 28-38 percent of the crop product, and in the market system 48 percent. Why these differences?

Part of the differences are undoubtedly due to inaccuracies in the data. In working with rough approximations, as was the case in deriving some of these estimates, differences in results of 5 or even 10 percentage points are not unexpectedly large. But there are grounds for believing that for rents and wages the discrepancy is real, even if the actual difference between the two sets of estimates is not exact, and that the discrepancy derives from the fact that in the two systems the principle of apportioning incomes is not the same. The reasons are partly that the discrepancy should be even larger, quantitatively, than that shown in the estimates, and partly that a difference between

TABLE 1

PROPORTIONS OF THE NET CROP PRODUCT IN 1951
RECEIVED BY LAND, LABOR AND CAPITAL
ACCORDING TO THE ESTIMATES BASED
ON MARKET VALUES AND THE SHARE SYSTEM

	Wages (1)	Returns to capital[c] (2)	Rents (3)	Total crop product (4)
Estimates based on market values[a]	48%	18%	33%	100%
Estimates based on the share system[b]	28-38%	9-19%	52%	100%

a. From Chapter II, Table 1 on p. 37 above.

b. From Chapter III, Table 3 on p. 52 above.

c. The return to capital in both systems includes some im-
    puted rent for work animals pastured on common land, but
    it excludes the return on land improvements such as ir-
    rigation, or the return from investments in trees. Such
    incomes are included with rent.

the two sets of estimates can be expected on logical grounds.

A. The Evidence of a Difference

The quantitative difference between wage and rent shares in the two systems of distribution should be greater than shown in Table 1 because the percentages for the market system in the table are too small for wages and too large for rents.

(1) Underestimate of wages in the market system. The estimate of wages in the market system is undoubtedly too low. Imputed wages in the market system were taken to be equal to the value of paid wages at harvest time, i.e., a value was ascribed to the labor of self-employed farmers for a period of only forty-five days. This was done because it was the only way in which the problem of seasonal underemployment could be handled since, as was previously noted, the marginal product of labor during periods of unemployment should be smaller than paid wages. Yet by taking the marginal product of labor as equal to the market value of only forty-five days work, there is no doubt that imputed wages were underestimated. The season of forty-five days represents the minimum period for which one could ascertain quite definitely that there is no unemployment, the harvest period being one of a labor shortage. This does not mean, however, that the marginal product of labor is zero during the whole of the remaining ten and a half months. The estimate of market wages is therefore too low, possibly by a considerable amount.

(2) Over-statement of the total crop product. In addition to understating market wages, the estimates also overstate the size of the total crop product, resulting in too large an income for the factor of production whose income is estimated as a residual, i.e., market

rents. The total crop product should be too large for two reasons. For one, according to the analysis done by the U.S. Department of Agriculture,[1] the post-1950 data on wheat output reported by the Central Statistical Office of Turkey (whose crop data serve as a basis for the Turkish national income estimates of the value of the gross crop product) are over-estimated, and should be reduced by about 20 percent to obtain more realistic values. The analysis of this problem by Abraham Hirsch and myself supports this conclusion,[2] and also shows that this reduction should be made for all cereals, since there is a very close correlation between wheat yields and all cereal yields in the estimates of the Central Statistical Office.

Another reason why the total crop product should be taken to be smaller than that given in the official data is that 1951 was a fine crop year with yields better than average. This would make little difference if the present estimates were only concerned with the specific year 1951, but this is not the case. The purpose of this study is to gauge how income was distributed "normally" during this period, i.e., if the large changes brought about by crop variations from year to year are abstracted from. Thus, since 1951 was a better than "normal" year, and rent had been computed above as a residual in the market estimates (and therefore came out larger than it could be expected to be "normally"), the "normalized" values of the distributive shares for the market system would deviate by a larger amount from those for the shares system than shown by the figures in Table 2 (see p.59).

An attempt in fact has been made to adjust for both factors considered in this section, first by reducing the cereal portion of this output and then normalizing this reduced gross output to adjust for variations in the weather. The resulting overall reduction is 10 percent for gross output, but larger--13 percent--for net

TABLE 2

REVISED DISTRIBUTION OF INCOME ACCORDING TO THE MARKET
SYSTEM (AFTER ADJUSTING THE TOTAL OUTPUT FOR OVER-
ESTIMATES IN CEREAL OUTPUT AND FOR TREND), AND
DISTRIBUTION OF INCOME ACCORDING TO THE
SHARES SYSTEM

	Factor shares estimated according to	
	the market system[a]	the shares system[b]
Wages	56%	28-38%
Return on investment	21%	9-19%
Rent	23%	52%
Total	100%	100%[c]

a. Computed by deducting from the national income origina-
    ting in crop production--the latter adjusted for over-
    estimates in cereal output and for variations in
    weather--of TL. 2,828 million, the return to labor and
    capital of TL. 1,577 million and TL. 600 million, which
    are shown in Chapter II, Table 1, and attributing the
    residual income of TL. 651 million to rent. The per-
    cent shares in this table were then calculated from
    these income estimates. For the adjustment in the nation-
    al income data see note 3 to this chapter.

b. This is the same distribution as that shown in Table 1
    of this chapter.

c. Percentages do not add to 100 due to rounding.

output.[3] (The adjustment in the net output is
larger because costs, which should for most part
be unaffected by variations or overestimates in
yields, become a larger portion of the gross value
if the latter is reduced.)

As a result of this adjustment the income shares in the market system change considerably. Rents become 23 percent of the net output, compared to the share of 33 percent estimated before the size of the crop product was
reduced. Since the share of rents is less, the
shares of the two other factors are increased,
from 48 to 56 percent for wages, and from 18 to 21
percent for the return to capital. It should be
pointed out, however, that these adjustments
still leave too small a share for wages--and
therefore too large a share for the other fac-
tors--since the shares in the market system were
only adjusted to correct for the overstatement
in the total income but not for the fact that
wages in the market system are also underestimated.

The new distribution of income according
to the market system is presented in Table 2
together with the distribution according to the
shares system to enable comparison. It is seen
that the discrepancy between the shares of wages
and rents in the two systems has now increased
to a range of between 18 and 28 percentage
points for wages (compared to the previous range
of 10 to 20 percentage points), and to 29 percentage points for rents (up from the previous
19 points). For reasons noted the actual discrepancy should be still larger than that shown.

B. Reasons for the Difference

Should one expect on rational grounds
that the shares system would distribute income
in approximately the same way as the market system does? One should if the shares arrangements
are relatively sensitive to market forces.

Otherwise even if the evidence should show that
the two systems did give the same results one
would have to conclude that it was only by coincidence.

The evidence suggests very strongly that
shares are insensitive to all but the strongest
of market forces and only those of certain kinds.
It was seen, for example, that when the mechanized farmer rents land, he pays the same proportion as others do even though the amount of rent
he pays is considerably greater. Where better
crops are grown the shares arrangements seem to
be somewhat affected by market forces but not by
nearly enough to give the factors their marginal
returns. The fifty-fifty system is very much the
predominant one and movements away from it seem
to be extremely "sticky,"[4] manifesting themselves
largely in the distribution of costs. Thus, on
rational grounds, too, the conclusion is reached
that even were there no inaccuracies in the data
one would still expect to find significant differences between the two sets of estimates.

C. Conclusion

Since the differences between the two
sets of estimates is almost certainly real, a
whole host of interesting theoretical questions
emerges. For example, how does the shares system affect the allocation of resources generally
when compared with the market system as a model?
More specifically: Would less land have been
left uncultivated in the relatively underpopula-
ted part of the country, Southeastern Anatolia
(particularly before tractors were introduced in
the late 1940's), had the market rather than the
shares system prevailed? Might the government
improve resource allocation by controlling the
shares at which land is rented out? More generally: When the income from the land is low,
as in arid regions, the landlord has the advantage with the shares system since rents under
the shares system do not differ very much wheth-

er the value of output produced on the land is low or high. But when the income from the land is high, the landlord has a disadvantage with the shares system compared with the market system for in that case, while the residual left for rent is very large, the high income is at least in part shared between the landlord and the tenant. This seems to explain why, in areas where the value of agricultural output has risen rapidly, the spread to the money economy in agriculture has been accelerated. An even more general question that is raised is how the transition from the shares to the market system as development occurs can be expected to affect income distribution and what effect this will have on the development process and on social welfare.

CHAPTER V

FUNCTIONAL DISTRIBUTION OF CROP
AND ANIMAL INCOMES

Animal incomes have not so far been included in
the estimates of functional income distribution.
In this chapter, therefore, the proportion of
this income going to land, labor, and capital
will be estimated. This will make it possible
at the end of the chapter to derive the functional distribution of crop and animal incomes combined. Since animal incomes derive from livestock raised on common land the share system in
this case does not apply; therefore the distribution of income from animals and animal products
will be estimated only according to the market
system.

I. Functional Distribution of Animal Incomes

A. The Return to Labor

The wage income derived from stock raising consists primarily of shepherd wages. Shepherd work lasts as long as the livestock are
pastured outdoors, which is about eight months
in Central Anatolia,[1] and somewhat less in the
eastern highlands where the climate is colder and
the pasturing season therefore shorter.[2] The
shepherds in Turkey are peasants with little or
no land who are hired by the villages. They get
paid a certain amount in money or kind for each
animal in their charge.[3]

From the data in the Village Study it is
found that paid wages amount to about 4 percent
of the sum of net factor incomes,[4] and that imputed shepherd wages are negligible.[5]

B.   The Return to Land

Pasture land in Turkey is common land and any villager can use the land belonging to his village without paying rent for its use. Rent, therefore, does not constitute an expense. This raises the question whether a part of the return from animal products constitutes imputed rent. The answer hinges on whether pasture land has scarcity value, which in turn depends on whether the number of animals pastured on the common land is limited or not. If, because pasture land can be freely used, the number of animals pastured on this land can increase without limit, then theoretically, pasture land should be treated as a free good and obtains no rent. According to economic theory, if the net return from animals pastured is higher than the net return from other types of investments, more and more animals would be pastured until diminishing returns reduce the investment return from the ownership of animals to a point where it is no longer higher than the return from other investments, and until, therefore, no imputed rent is left.

If the average return per animal falls, diminishing returns on the last animal grazed are involved, although if more and more animals are added to the pastures, the total return from animals may increase at the same time, but less than in proportion to the number of animals. However it is also possible that there is an absolute decline in the total return so that marginal returns are negative. This situation could arise for two reasons. (1) So long as the average return on investments in animals is greater than that from other investments, it would pay individual peasants to increase the number of animals even though the marginal return is negative. (2) The small peasant may have limited investment opportunities. If he has more income to invest he may increase the

number of his livestock even though the return
he receives is very low.

To what extent these theoretical considerations are borne out in reality depends on
several factors. The first is whether villages
impose restrictions on the number of animals that
any villager may pasture on the village commons.
The little information on this question that is
available, based on a few references in publications and the opinion of persons generally
familiar with Turkish agriculture, suggest that
villages impose such restrictions only to a limited extent, if at all.[6] The effect of having
inadequate or no restrictions in most of the
country is made evident by the fact that the pastures are heavily over-grazed, suggesting that
aggregate output has been reduced.[7] The effect
of the over-grazing is described vividly in
Turkey, Country Report, as follows: "Whereas
the steppe used to turn green twice a year, in
spring and in autumn, it is now nearly impossible,
in autumn, to describe the steppe as green even
if abundant rain does fall. Grazing animals are
so seriously underfed that it is surprising that
they stay alive, let alone produce products useful to man."[8]

The over-grazing of pasture land has
come about not only by increases in the number
of animals pastured. Common land can also be
put under cultivation by villagers who need it
or, probably more often, by those who are influ-
ential in the village. As a result more and more
common land has been taken over by farms as the
years have passed (as shown in Table 1, see
page 66) and the amount and quality of the pasture land left have been greatly reduced. The
plowing up of the common land took place at the
same time that the number of animals pastured
increased (Table 2, see page 67.) Both of these
developments together have caused the overgrazing, and an apparently negative return on the
marginal animal grazed.

All that has been said does not prove,

TABLE 1

INCREASE IN AREA CULTIVATED AND REDUCTION IN
AREA OF PASTURE LAND, 1938-1960

	Area cultivated[a]		Meadows and pastures	
	In millions of hectares[b]	Index 1938= 100	In millions of hectares[b]	Index 1938= 100
	(1)	(2)	(3)	(4)
1938	14.5	100	41.1	100
1948	15.4	106	38.3	93
1951	17.2	119	37.0	90
1953	21.1	146	33.3	81
1958	24.7	170	29.1	71
1960	25.3	174	28.7	70

a. Includes area of fields and fallow, as well as orchards, gardens, vineyards, and olive groves.

b. Source: Monthly Bulletin of Statistics, No. 64, p. 135, and No. 88, p. 151.

TABLE 2

TOTAL NUMBER OF NON-WORK ANIMALS GRAZED IN
TURKEY EXPRESSED IN GRAZING UNITS
OF CATTLE EQUIVALENTS, 1938-1960[a]

	Animals grazed in millions of grazing units[b]	Index, 1938 = 100
938	20.3	100
948	22.6	111
951	23.1	114
953	24.2	119
958	27.7	136
960	28.7	141

[a]. Including, however, cattle and buffalos used for work because the number of work and non-work animals among them could not readily be separated.

[b]. The number of each type of non-work animal (but see qualification in note a) given in the Monthly Bulletin of Statistics, No. 34-6, p. 177, and No. 88, p. 159, were converted into grazing units in cattle equivalents by assigning the following cattle equivalents to different types of animals: sheep 0.25, goats 0.25, Angora goats 0.17, buffalos 1.7. Cattle, of course, are 1.0 cattle equivalents. These ratios were indicated by Nicolas Helburn in Some Trends in the (sic) Turkish Agriculture (Ankara: Doğuş Ltd., 1953).

however, that total imputed rents are zero. The existence of absolute diminishing returns merely means that the total imputed rents are smaller than they would otherwise be, but unless the negative returns go so far as to offset all positive returns, there may still, on the average, be positive imputed rents. The elimination of all imputed rents would only be effected if farmers increased the number of animals pastured, or reduced the amount of land available for pasturing, to the point where the return from investments in animals is no greater than the return on other types of investment. This in turn depends on the opportunity that farmers have for either plowing up the pasture land or increasing the number of animals.

The opportunity for plowing up pasture land seems to have been fairly unrestricted, as evidenced by the tremendous decline in pasture land and the corresponding increase in crop land shown in Table 1,[9] and it has been suggested that the new land put under cultivation has been of such increasingly poor quality that a substantial part of this land should be restored to pastures.[10] Thus the trend in this direction seems to have gone very far. One cannot tell from this, however, how far this practice has gone to reduce the return on the pasture land left.

So far as the opportunity that farmers have for increasing their livestock is concerned, this is certainly limited. The main limitation here is the farmer's ability to feed the animals through the winter months. Since the winter feed of non-work animals (and to a large extent also of work animals) consists almost exclusively of straw, mixed with grain only to the extent to which the primitive methods of threshing and winnowing fail to separate all seed from the straw,[11] the amount of feed, and therefore the number of animals that can be fed, depends on the size of the cereal crop rather than on the number of animals that can be supported by the pastures during the non-winter months, at least up to a point.[12] The practice of supporting non-work animals on straw during the winter probably explains why the number of animals has increased when the amount of pasture land decreased, since the reduction in the amount of pastures has meant an increased amount of land put to cereal cultivation, and therefore a greater production of straw for winter feed.

Since the production of winter feed sets a limit to the number of animals that can be pastured, it is likely that farmers, on the average, did not have the opportunity to increase their livestock enough to eliminate all imputed rent on pasture land unless this process was helped by the decline in the amount of pasture land. But since in the years after 1951, the year to which the estimates in Part I of this book refer, the amount of pasture land has continued to decline and the number of animals to increase (see Tables 1 and 2), it is likely that there was still some imputed rent left on pasture land in 1951.

This poses a problem for the present calculations since there is no way of estimating how large the size of imputed rent was at that time. The best that can be done is to take imputed rent as zero, and to note that the return on investment that can be computed probably includes some imputed rent in addition to pure investment income.

C. The Return to Capital

The return to capital should be the residual after wages and rents are deducted from the net income. The residual income is 96 percent of the net income, since estimated wages were 4 percent and rents were taken to be zero. It should be borne in mind that the actual return to capital should be somewhat lower because of the presence of some imputed rents.

D. The Total Income from Animal Products

Were the objective of these estimates
limited to obtaining a functional distribution
of animal incomes alone, the proportions derived
above would suffice. However, the estimates for
animal incomes will also be used to derive a
functional distribution of both crop and animal
incomes, and for this purpose the proportions
must be converted to lira amounts--so that they
can be added to the crop lira shares--and here
a problem arises. In the previous chapter reason was found to adjust the official estimate of
crop income downward. There is evidence to indicate that the size of the animal income in the
national income accounts is also too large, and
probably by a larger proportion than crop incomes. First, as shown in Appendix C, the total
value of animal incomes in the national income
statistics implies a rate of return on the
value of the investment needed to produce this
income of 100 percent, compared to the far more
reasonable rate of only 34 percent calculated fr
the data in the Village Study. Although there
could have been some under-reporting in the Village Study, the remarkable consistency of the
livestock data in this study (shown in Appendix
C) leads one to doubt that the under-reporting
error could be considerable. In addition, as wi
be shown in Chapter VIII, the income from animal
products in the national income accounts is quit
definitely too large to be consistent with other
data.

The reason why animal incomes are overestimated in these statistics is that no account
was taken of the fact that overgrazing should
have led to a decline in imputed rents on pastur
land and therefore in the return per animal pastured. No data were available for estimating
directly the output of animal products produced
and consumed in villages when the national income methodology was first worked out, and for
this reason the statisticians at the Central

Statistical Office estimated the output of animal products by adapting formulas to Turkish conditions that had been used in some European countries. These consisted of estimating how many offspring a herd of 100 females would be expected to produce ayear, the number that would die a natural death, etc. For the years in question, and also thereafter,[13] these formulas had not been modified to take account of the pressure on the communal pasture land and the resulting decline in the value of output produced on this land. Thus the value of the product of animals estimated in the national income data seems more closely to reflect the value that would have been produced if the income yielded by the pasture land had not declined absolutely, than the value actually produced in 1051.

Unfortunately, no good basis exists for revising the value of animal incomes. Since it is very likely that the overestimate is greater for animal than for crop incomes, and since crop income had been reduced to adjust for overstatement in the last chapter, were no adjustment made for the overestimate of animal incomes, the over-all result of combining the functional distributions of crop and animal incomes would be badly distorted. Although the extent by which animal incomes are overestimated cannot be determined, these incomes were adjusted downward by the same proportion as were crop incomes in the last chapter. This adjustment helps to prevent distorting the ratio of crop to animal incomes even more than is apparently the case in the national income statistics, although the resulting weight attributed to animal incomes in the combined functional distribution of crop and animal incomes should still be too large. The lira shares of the factors after the adjustment was made, as well as the proportions, are shown in Table 3 (see page 72).

TABLE 3

FUNCTIONAL DISTRIBUTION OF NET INCOME FROM
ANIMALS AND ANIMAL PRODUCTS

	In millions of TL.	As percent of total
Wages	71	4%
Rent	0	0%
Return to capital	1,700	96%
Total	1,771	100%

II. The Distribution of the Total Crop and Animal Product

It is now possible to add the distribution of the income derived from animals to the distribution of the crop product estimated in Chapters II and III to obtain the over-all distribution of crop and animal products. Since two distributions for the crop product were derived two over-all distributions are obtained as well.

In Table 4 (see page 74) the distribution of animal incomes is added to the crop incomes distributed according to the market system and to the shares system. According to the first distribution, wages are shown to receive 36 percent of the combined agricultural product, capital 50 percent, and rent 14 percent. According to the second, wages receive 19-25 percent, capital 42-49 percent, and rent 33 percent.

In both distributions the income going to capital constitutes one half, or nearly one half, of the total income, while rent and wages together get roughly the other half. This suggests that capital is the most important source of income in Turkish agriculture. The importance of capital should be somewhat smaller than shown in these distributions because the total of animal incomes, as has been shown, should be too high and the return to capital constitutes such a very large portion of animal income. But even if the total income from animals and animal products were reduced by one-half--probably an extreme adjustment for 1951--the return to capital would still constitute about one third of the total agricultural income,[14] and is, therefore, still very large. However, the return to labor and to land should be somewhat higher than shown in Table 4.

TABLE 4

FUNCTIONAL DISTRIBUTIONS OF TOTAL INCOME
ORIGINATING IN CROP AND ANIMAL PRODUCTION

	Factor shares if crop incomes are estimated according to:	
	the market system[a]	the shares system[b]
Wages	36%	19-25%
Return to capital	50%	49-42%
Rent	14%	33%
Total	100%	100%[c]

---

a. Derived by adding the distribution of crop incomes in
   Chapter IV, Table 2 (on p. 59) to the distribution of
   animal incomes in Table 3 of this Chapter (on p. 72).
   To do so the shares going to land, labor, and capital in
   each of the two distributions were expressed in money,
   and added; after that the resulting money totals for
   each factor were converted into percents of the combined
   total income from crops and animals of TL. 4,599 million
   (TL. 2,828 million for crops, and TL. 1,771 for animals).

b. Derived by adding the distribution of crop incomes in
   Chapter III, Table 3 (on p. 52) to the distribution of
   animal incomes in Table 3 of this chapter. The factor
   shares were first added in lira and the results were
   then converted into percents of the combined total income from crops and animals of TL. 4,599 million.
   (See note a above.)

c. Percentages on the left do not add to 100 due to
   rounding.

PART II

DISTRIBUTION OF INCOME

BY INCOME SIZES

In Part I the distribution of agricultural incomes has been estimated according to functional shares received by each of the factors of production. However, in Turkey land is widely owned, and the incomes of rich and poor peasants are not, on the whole, derived from the ownership of different factors of production, as would be the case in a country where the land is owned by a class of landlords and worked by a class of landless peasants. For this reason the analysis of incomes by factors does not shed light on the distribution of income between rich and poor reasants. In this part of the study, therefore, the attempt will be made to find out how incomes are distributed among the agricultural population by size of income earned.

A. The Two Major Distributions That Will Be Derived

A problem encountered at the outset has to do with the way the distribution of agricultural income is to be conceived. Some conceptions must be ruled out from the start. Agricultural income was defined in the last part as the total income originating in agriculture; this definition is no longer appropriate for this part of the study. One reason is that some of the income originating in agriculture is earned by persons who live permanently in cities (primarily absentee landlords),[1] and it is not possible to allocate this income among income brackets as data are not available to determine how many absentee landlords there are or how much income from rent and other sources each of them earns.

(1) One way to resolve this problem is to define agricultural income as that portion of net income originating in agriculture which those who operate farms earn from their operations. Income so defined differs from total income originating in agriculture by the amount of wages earned by landless peasants or by farm

operators who do seasonal work for other farmers, and by the amount of rent earned by absentee land-lords.

(2) The distribution of agricultural in-come can also be conceived of as the distribution of the total income earned by those who are pri-marily engaged in agricultural pursuits. Such a distribution would differ from (1) by counting landless farmers with income earners, and by in-cluding with income not only earnings that farm-ers derive from their own operations, but the total income of farm households, regardless of whether it originates in the agricultural sector or not. Since distribution (1) constitutes an important component of distribution (2), the former is estimated first, but is later changed to incorporate the additional incomes necessary to derive distribution(2).

B. Approach to the Problem

Whichever concept is used, any attempt to estimate a size distribution of income among farm families runs into the problem that no data on income distribution in agriculture are avail-able. One must, therefore, resort to indirect methods. The only available statistics that have a bearing on inequality in agriculture by size are data on the distribution of land operated, and therefore these will be used as a point of departure. But amount of land operated is not the only determinant of size of income among farmers, and to the extent to which other fac-tors enter it is necessary to modify the first rough approach to a distribution of income based only on the distribution of land operated.

Size of income and size of land operated can be unrelated, only imperfectly related, or even inversely related if the following condi-tions prevail:

1. The two distributions should be only imperfectly related if the soil and climate vary

in different regions. This point is very significant for Turkey, a country that covers a relatively large geographic area, with dry parts and rainy ones, cold and warm ones. Because of this diversity a great variety of crops are grown in Turkey, and the incomes from these different crops are not likely to be the same for each decare of land operated.

2. The two distributions are only imperfectly related if large farmers use better methods of production than small ones do. This may result in greater output per decare, but also involve greater costs. In addition, large farmers may grow different crops from small ones because the former produce for the market while the latter produce for home consumption. Different crops again may result in different incomes per decare of land operated.

3. The relation between the two distributions is also imperfect because regardless of methods and types of crops grown, the large farmer must pay wages while the small one does not. To this extent the net income per decare of land operated for large farmers should be smaller than that of the small farmer.

4. Again the two distributions are only imperfectly related if some farmers own their farms and others must pay rent.

5. The distribution of income derived from animals is likely to bear only an imperfect relation to the distribution of land operated. Although during the winter animals must be supported with feed grown on farm land, during the summer they are grazed on common land.

6. What has been said so far refers to income of farm operators from their operations (concept 1). If the objective is to derive a distribution of all income earned by farm families (using concept 2), further qualifications must be added. Farm operators receive incomes from rent for land they own and rent out, from work they do for other farmers, and from non-

agricultural sources (in money and via imputation). Finally, landless farmers receive incomes which must be taken into account. None of this income can be expected to be distributed precisely as is size of land operated.

This is a rather formidable list of qualifications. If size of land operated is to be taken as a point of departure for estimating the distribution of income among farmers by income size, all of these qualifications must be dealt with, and they will be in turn. This means that the distribution of land operated will have to be modified step by step, each modification being one move in the desired direction, and it is only in the last chapter of Part II that the final distribution will emerge.

The procedure used to derive the distribution of income by size is therefore the following: In Chapters VI and VII the distribution of crop incomes alone will be derived, in the first of these two chapters the gross distribution, and in the second the net. (This involves dealing with the qualifications mentioned in points 1, 2, 3, and 4 above.) Chapter VIII will modify these findings to allow for the addition of animal incomes. (This involves dealing with qualification 5.) The distribution that will be derived at the end of Chapter VIII is that of crop and animal incomes net of all paid expenses, including costs that are factor incomes, such as rent, wages, and interest. In other words, income up to then will have been defined as the income earned by farm operators from their operations. Moreover, only the shape (proportions of total income) of this distribution is derived in Chapter VIII. The corresponding money earnings of each tenth of farm operators are calculated in Section I of Chapter IX after the total income to which this distribution refers has been determined.

These estimates are further modified in Section II of Chapter IX to derive the distribution of income from all sources earned by all farm families. This involves adding to the previous distribution all agricultural and non-agricultural incomes earned by farmers which had so far been omitted, and taking account of the earnings of landless farm workers. (These estimates deal with the qualifications mentioned in point 6.) As a conclusion to Part II, the major factors that make for more or less inequality in the size distribution of income among farmers will be summarized and used at the same time to interpret the effect on income distribution of some recent changes in the agricultural sector. This is done in the last section of Chapter IX.

CHAPTER VI

THE SHAPE OF THE DISTRIBUTION
OF GROSS CROP INCOMES

The first estimate is the derivation of a distribution of gross crop incomes. For the moment,
therefore, the effect on income distribution of
agricultural incomes other than crops is omitted,
and so is the effect on income distribution of
crop costs.

I. First Approximation: Assuming Equal
Gross Incomes per
Decare Within Provinces

Table 1 (see page 83) gives a summary
of the data on the distribution of land operated
which is used as a point of departure for the
estimates.[1] This distribution would be identical with the distribution of gross crop incomes
if the gross return from crops were proportional
to the size of land operated, i.e., if every decare of land produced the same gross income.
This, if course, is not the case, particularly
in a country like Turkey where temperature and
rainfall differ very markedly from one part of
the country to the other. As a consequence there
are great variations in the types of crops grown
in different parts of the country and in the a-
mount of land that needs to be left fallow every
year in different areas, both of which should
cause very large differences in the amount of
income that different farmers can derive from a
farm of the same size. But it is likely that
soil, temperature, and rainfall vary much less
within small areas than they do between them.
Therefore, if the country could be divided into
small, and for present purposes, relatively homogeneous areas, and if these areas could be used
as the basic units in the calculations, one could

TABLE 1

PERCENT OF LAND OPERATED BY EACH
TENTH OF FARM FAMILIES[a]

Percent of all rural farm families	Percent of all land operated
Lowest 10%	
	} 1.8
2nd lowest 10%	
3rd lowest 10%	2.1
4th lowest 10%	3.2
5th lowest 10%	4.5
6th lowest 10%	5.7
7th lowest 10%	7.5
8th lowest 10%	10.1
9th lowest 10%	15.3
Highest 10%	49.8
All families	100.0

Total amount of land operated = 194,520,000 decares

Total number of rural farm families = 2,527,800

---

a. From 1950 Census of Agriculture, Table 8. In the table
    above, the figures were rearranged into deciles.

make a reasonable estimate of gross incomes on the basis of average figures.

The procedure used was the following: The data in Table 1 on land operation are available for sixty-one of Turkey's sixty-three provinces. Each of these provinces is small enough for it to be reasonable to assume that they are relatively homogeneous with respect to temperature and rainfall. Data are available, too, from which the average gross income per decare in each of these sixty-one provinces can be calculated. By multiplying the average number of decares of each land bracket (i.e. size distribution of farms) in a given province by the average gross crop income per decare of crop land in that province, and then repeating these calculations for each province, some 600 figures on gross crop incomes were derived, one for each land bracket in each province. These figures were arranged into a new frequency distribution by grouping them according to size of farm income together with the number of families that correspond to each income group. The new distribution is shown in Table 2 (see p. 85). It should, by and large, incorporate the differences in the gross crop incomes per decare that exist between provinces because of variations in yields, in types of crops grown, and in fallow land. Of course, the differences in the incomes per decare of large and small farmers within provinces are not taken into account in the new distribution. They are considered in Section II of this chapter.

The results shown in Table 2 are rather surprising, for the distribution is more unequal than that of land operated and this is quite contrary to what is generally believed. It is well known that in some regions, such as the provinces along the Black Sea, even small farms may earn quite good incomes if they grow crops, like tea, which yield a very high return per decare. The results, however, are not inconsistent with the proposition that small but high-income farms

TABLE 2

DISTRIBUTION OF GROSS INCOME FROM CROPS IN TURKEY
BY TENTHS. FIRST APPROXIMATION: ASSUMING
EQUAL INCOMES PER DECARE
WITHIN PROVINCES[a]

Percent of all farm families	Percent of total gross crop income
Lowest 10%	0.86
2nd lowest 10%	1.29
3rd lowest 10%	2.11
4th lowest 10%	3.00
5th lowest 10%	3.83
6th lowest 10%	5.08
7th lowest 10%	6.72
8th lowest 10%	9.06
9th lowest 10%	13.53
Highest 10%	54.51
	100.00[c]

Total number of families = 2,527,800
Total income = TL. 6,209,490,400[b]

a. Computed by weighting the farms in the distribution of
land operated by the average gross crop income per decare
of the provinces in which these farms are located. Specifically: The 1950 Agricultural Census Results, pp. 134-
5, show for 61 provinces the number of families and the
amount of land operated in each of 10 land brackets.
From this it was possible to compute the average amount
of land operated in each of these land brackets and in
each province. This gave somewhat less than 610 fig-

ures as in some provinces some land brackets were vacant. These figures were then multiplied by the average gross crop income per decare of the province in which each of these hundreds of average size farms were located. The results were arranged in order of magnitude, multiplied by the number of families that correspond to each land size bracket, the values were regrouped, and the figures shown in the table were computed from this distribution.

The average gross crop income per decare per province, used in these calculations, was derived by dividing the gross crop income for each province by the total area cultivated in the same province. The gross crop income per province is given in: Türkiye Zirai İstihsal Kıymeti 1952, p. 4. The area cultivated per province was calculated from data published in Agricultural Structure and Production, 1946-1953, Turkey, Central Statistical Office, Publication No. 351, pp. 3-4, and area cultivated for each province was taken to be the total of: area sown, fallow land, orchards and gardens, olive groves. In Agricultural Structure and Production no data are reported on fallow land for the provinces of Aydın, Hakâri, Muğla, Rize, Samsun, Seyhan, Trabzon. As a result the average gross crop income per decare for these provinces calculated from the given figures should be somewhat too high. No adjustment was made for these overstatements, however, because: 1. Except for Hakâri the percent of fallow land to area cultivated should be small as all these provinces, except Hakâri, are located in coastal areas and thus get considerably more rainfall than the average in the country. 2. So far as Hakâri is concerned, this province is not included in the computations of income distribution as this is one of the two provinces omitted in the distribution of land operation. 3. The effect of overstating the gross incomes in these provinces on the over-all distribution of income should roughly cancel out since Seyhan is one of the provinces that include the largest farms and very few small ones, while Rize and Trabzon represent the reverse picture, and the remaining provinces are in between.

b. The true total income of this distribution is
    TL. 5,363,356,300 and the true mean income TL. 2,122,
    i.e., both the true total and the true mean are 16%
    lower than shown above. For the reasons for this overstatement, see Appendix E.

c. Percentages do not add up to 100% due to rounding.

are to be found in some of the more fertile areas.
The average income per decare applied to some of
the Black Sea provinces where the average farm
is much smaller than in most provinces, was indeed among the highest,[2] and if one computes the
average gross crop income of each of the land
brackets in the distribution of land operated in
Table 1, one finds that small farms generally
had a higher income per decare than the average
in the nation.[3] However, large farms, too, are
situated to a large extent in high-income areas.
Thus, almost 50 percent of the number of farms
with over 500 decares are located in the Aegean
and the Mediterranean, the two regions among
Turkey's nine with the highest average income
per decare, and more important, in terms of
area cultivated, over 50 percent of the area of
farms with over 500 decares is located in these
two highest-income regions.[4] The fact that
these two regions had such a high income per decare is explained partly by the relatively high
proportion of industrial crops that is grown in
these regions, which give considerably better
than average incomes per decare. Thus 40 percent and 45 percent respectively of the total
gross crop income in the Mediterranean and Aegean came from industrial crops compared with a
national average of only 26 percent; and industrial crops yielded an average gross income per
decare of TL. 120, compared with an average for
all crops of TL. 28. Another reason is that
less land needs to be left fallow in these two
regions than is necessary in the interior.[5]

        Thus in the first approximation it turns
out that the distribution of gross crop incomes
is more unequal than the distribution of land
operated because large farms are located in
areas in which the income per decare is higher
than the average in the nation to an even larger
extent than are small farms.

II. Differences in Gross Crop Incomes per Decare Within Provinces

The computations described so far have assigned to all farms situated in the same province the average gross crop income per decare in that province, i.e., they took account of the differences in income per decare between provinces; within each province the gross income per decare of large and small farms was taken to be the same. This assumption must now be relaxed. One would expect that large farms generally use better methods such as mechanical aids, and have better land than small ones. In addition, since large farmers practice commercial rather than subsistence farming, one would expect that they grow more crops that give a high return on the market. In this section the effect of mechanization on income distribution will be considered first, then the effects of factors other than mechanization, assuming provisionally that large and small farmers grow the same crops, and finally, the effects of differences in crops grown.

A. Differences Due to Mechanization

In Chapter I it was noted that mechanization increases yields in Turkey because it enables more timely cultivation of the soil (which affects yield), and gives the farmer more time to plow his fallow during the limited period available for the plowing of both the crop land and fallow land. It has also been observed that mechanization increases yields because it enables better seedbed preparation, more efficient use of fertilizer, and reduction of harvest losses.[6] The extent to which mechanization affects income distribution therefore depends on (1) the extent to which it increases the yield of the mechanized (large) farmer, and (2) the degree to which large farmers are mechanized. These factors will be considered in turn.

1. In the Mechanization Study informa-

tion was derived on the gross yields of mechanized and unmechanized farmers. The pertinent
results are shown in Table 3 (see p. 90).
It is seen that on the average mechanization increased yields by 39 percent (50.6/36.5).

2.   The extent to which mechanization
increases the incomes of large farmers depends
not only on the increased yields but also on the
number of these farmers who own tractors.   If
they constitute only a small minority of the
large farms, the effect of mechanization on income distribution would be negligible. But if
most large farms are mechanized, the effect
would be quite considerable.

The proportion of the area of large farms
that is cultivated with tractors was estimated
from the available data on the number of tractors
in the country,[7] the estimated average area cultivated per tractor in the Mechanization Study,[8]
and the total cultivated area of farms with over
500 decares.[9] By assuming provisionally that
tractors are only used on farms with over 500
decares, it was found that the total area worked
with tractors constituted 45 percent of the area
of farms with over 500 decares. However, since
some farms with less than 500 decares also use
tractors, this percentage should be too high as
an indication of the area cultivated with tractors on large farms only.[10] No data are available which would enable one to estimate precisely what proportion of all tractors are used
by smaller farms, and therefore to what extent
the figure of 45 percent is overstated. It was
arbitrarily reduced to 40 percent.

B.   Differences in Yields Due to Factors Other
than Mechanization

But aside from the rather substantial
increases caused by mechanization, there is no
evidence that large farmers get better yields
than small ones. Thus, as shown in Table 4
(see page 91) where the yields for unmechan-

TABLE 3

GROSS INCOME PER DECARE OF FARMS IN THE
MECHANIZATION STUDY WITH MECHANIZED
AND UNMECHANIZED YIELDS
(In TL.)

Regions	With unmechanized yields	With mechanized yields
	(1)	(2)
Central Anatolia	18.5	24.8
Mediterranean	48.9	70.7
Aegean	110.7	159.2
Marmara	29.0	37.5
South East Anatolia	16.6	19.3
Black Sea	28.0	40.1
Total	36.5	50.6
Index	100	139

Source: Mechanization Study. For details of the computations see Table 1, Appendix D.

TABLE 4

REGIONAL COMPARISON OF AVERAGE YIELDS OF ALL FARMERS AND OF YIELDS
REPORTED IN THE MECHANIZATION STUDY IN 1952 (kg. per decare)[a]

Regions	Average yields in the region	Yields from the Mechanization Study as reported by village heads for	
		non-mechanized agriculture	mechanized agriculture
		WHEAT YIELDS	
	(1)[b]	(2)[c]	(3)[d]
Central Anatolia	112	128	176
Mediterranean	126	131	162
Aegean	106	164	185
Marmara	113	112	156
S. E. Anatolia	119	118	134
Black Sea	142	140	179
Average[k]	117	129	162
		BARLEY YIELDS	
	(4)[b]	(5)[e]	(6)[f]
Central Anatolia	119	165	208
Mediterranean	133	160	187
Aegean	109	193	207
Marmara	135	126	168
S. E. Anatolia	167	135	154
Black Sea	179	141	195
Average	134	157	187
		COTTON YIELDS	
	(7)[b]	(8)[g]	(9)[h]
Central Anatolia	-	-	-
Mediterranean	63	48	71
Aegean	109	115	168
Marmara	72	82	111
S. E. Anatolia	67	43	56
Black Sea	-	-	-
Average	73	61	85
		SUGAR BEET YIELDS	
	(10)[b]	(11)[i]	(12)[j]
Central Anatolia	2,405	2,571	3,286
Mediterranean	-	-	-
Aegean	-	-	-
Marmara	1,356	1,468	2,568
S. E. Anatolia	-	-	-
Black Sea	2,397	1,944	3,444
Average	2,225	2,377	3,166

a. In the Mechanization Study the same questions on yields of the four crops were addressed to the village heads and the sample farmers. The data in this table are only those given by the village heads which were, in most cases, higher than those given by the sample families. But the answers of the village heads are likely to be more reliable as the sample families might have tried to under-report their yields.

b. Computed by dividing the total output of each of the four crops in each region in 1952 by the area sown to the crop in each region in 1951/2. Each region was taken to include only those provinces which are included in these regions in Mechanization Study, Table 1 i.e., only the provinces in which sample farms were located. These computations are made from data given in _Agricultural Structure and Production, 1946-1954_, pp. 34-161. No adjustment was made in these data to take into account that the cereal yields of the Central Statistical Office are overestimated. If this adjustment were made, the yields in columns (1) and (4) would, on the average, be about 9% lower. (For the reasons and the magnitude of the overestimate in cereal yields, see pp. 57-58 above.

c. Mechanization Study, Table 73.

d. _Ibid._, Table 73.

e. _Ibid._, Table 76.

f. _Ibid._, Table 76.

g. _Ibid._, Table 79.

h. _Ibid._, Table 79.

i. _Ibid._, Table 82.

j. _Ibid._, Table 82.

k. The average yields shown in the Mechanization Study for each of the six regions have been averaged by using the weights developed in Appendix B, pp. 197-98.

ized agriculture reported by the sample farmers
(who for the most part are large farmers) in the
Mechanization Study are compared with the average
yield for these crops estimated by the Central
Statistical Office for the same provinces, one
finds that the yields reported by the farmers in
the Mechanization Study are higher for wheat and
barley, lower for cotton, and about the same for
beets. On the average, as shown in Table 5
(see page 94) this results in no significantly
higher yields. The data in the Village Study
also indicate that the yields of large farmers
are higher only because of mechanization. Thus
in the Village Study where wheat and barley
yields are given by farm size brackets as shown
in Table 6 (see page 95) yields are highest for
the largest farms. But these yields are lower
than they should be if one considers to what extent mechanization increases yields in Central
Anatolia and the degree to which these farms are
mechanized.[11] Thus factors other than mechanization apparently give the large farms in the Village Study lower yields than those obtained by
small ones.

Thus, contrary to expectation, the evidence suggests that large unmechanized farmers
either do not use better methods or do not have
better land, or that they may use better methods
but that this advantage is roughly offset by
having worse land, or that they have better land
but use less efficient methods. At any rate,
except for mechanization, assuming that the
same crops are grown, large farmers appear to
receive somewhat worse yields in Central Anatolia, but on the average in the country about
the same yields per decare as small farmers.[12]

C. Differences Due to Types of Crops Grown

Yield, as noted, is not the only factor
affecting income per decare. The types of crops
grown may be even more important, as the variations in income per decare for different crops

TABLE 5

GROSS INCOMES PER DECARE FROM THE FOUR CROPS GROWN IN
THE MECHANIZATION STUDY, COMPUTED WITH THE
AVERAGE YIELDS OF THESE CROPS IN EACH
REGION, AND WITH THOSE SHOWN IN THE
STUDY FOR UNMECHANIZED AGRICULTURE
(In TL.)

Regions	Gross incomes per decare	
	computed with the average yields of the four crops in each region	computed with the yields of unmechanized agriculture shown in the Mechanization Study
	(1)	(2)
Central Anatolia	15.9	18.5
Mediterranean	61.7	48.9
Aegean	102.7	110.7
Marmara	28.0	29.0
South East Anatolia	18.6	16.6
Black Sea	31.0	28.0
Average, all regions	36.3[a]	36.5
Index	100	101

Source: For sources and details about these computations see Appendix D, Table 1.

a. The yields used to compute column (1) are based on those of the Central Statistical Office, and should be too high for cereals. Therefore the average for all regions was adjusted to correct for this overstatement. Without this adjustment, the average in column (1) would be TL. 38.5.

TABLE 6

YIELDS FROM WHEAT AND BARLEY IN THE
VILLAGE STUDY BY FARM SIZES[a]
(In kg. per decare)

Farms by land size brackets (in decares)	Wheat yields (1)	Barley yields (2)
10 - 79	104	132
80 - 159	99.8	117
160 - 499	107.6	133
500 and over	120	137
Average all farms[b]	104	130

a. Village Study, Table 6.

b. The weights used to calculate this average reflect the relative importance of farms in each of the land brackets above as shown for regions I and IX (roughly the area covered by the Village Study survey) in 1950 Agricultural Census Results, p. 124. The area cultivated by the farmers in each of these land brackets in the Village Study was not used as weights, since, as noted previously, the Village Study sample includes an unrepresentatively high proportion of large farms.

are far greater than are the variations in yield
for the same crops.[13] It was noted previously
that large farmers would be expected to grow
crops that give a higher gross income per decare than the small ones. The evidence in Table
7 (see page 97) seems to bear out this conjec-
ture. The table gives by regions (1) the total
area of two cereals, wheat and barley, which
give a low return per decare, and of two industrial crops, cotton and beets, which give a high
income per decare; and (2) the area that is
planted to these crops by the farmers in the
Mechanization Study in the same regions. The
third column shows the percentage of the area of
these crops in the region sown by the mechanized
farmers, and shows that these farmers grew a
smaller proportion of the total wheat and barley
crop in each region than they did of the total
beet and cotton crop. For example, in the Mediterranean the farmers in the Mechanization Study
operated 12.19 percent of the total area sown to
cotton and beets in the provinces included in the
region, but only 4.58 percent of the wheat and
barley area. Note that this relationship holds
in all regions for which this comparison is made,
i.e., in all six regions the mechanized farmers
planted a higher proportion of the total crop
area to the two industrial crops and a lower proportion to the two cereal crops. Since the
mechanized farmers on the average are also large
farmers, the data in Table 7 suggest that the
large farmers concentrate on higher income crops
to a larger extent than do the average farmers
in the same region.

The over-all average in Table 8 (see
page 98) further supports this conclusion.
By comparing column (2) with column (1) in the
table, it is seen that the farmers in the Mechanization Study received 41 percent higher gross
incomes per decare (36.3/25.8) than the average
farmer in these regions. Since in these calculations the farmers in the Mechanization Study have
been attributed the average yields (in kg. per

TABLE 7

AREA SOWN TO WHEAT AND BARLEY AND TO COTTON AND BEETS
BY MECHANIZED FARMERS AND BY ALL FARMERS IN 1952
(In hectares)

	By the farmers in the Mechaniza-tion Study[a]	By all farmers in the same provinces[b]	Column (1) as percent of column (2)
	(1)	(2)	(3)
Central Anatolia			
Wheat and barley	38,731	2,348,375	1.65
Cotton and beets	187	8,097	2.31
Mediterranean			
Wheat and barley	17,507	382,572	4.58
Cotton and beets	47,139	386,795	12.19
Aegean			
Wheat and barley	6,884	326,487	2.11
Cotton and beets	21,095	174,965	12.06
Marmara			
Wheat and barley	11,811	412,222	2.87
Cotton and beets	1,785	28,510	6.26
South East Anatolia			
Wheat and barley	45,756	602,560	7.59
Cotton and beets	4,194	23,743	17.66
Black Sea			
Wheat and barley	1,413	215,279	0.66
Cotton and beets	179	7,341	2.43

a. Mechanization Study, Table 59.

b. Agricultural Structure and Production, 1946-1954,
    pp. 34-161.

TABLE 8

COMPARISON OF INCOME PER DECARE FROM ALL CROPS GROWN IN THE
REGION WITH INCOME PER DECARE FROM THE CROPS GROWN
BY THE FARMERS IN THE MECHANIZATION STUDY
(In TL.)

Regions	Average income per decare in each region from all crops (1)	Income per decare of the farmers in the Mechanization Study from their 4 crops assuming that they obtained the average yields in their regions for each of the 4 crops[a] (2)
Central Anatolia	20.4	15.9
Mediterranean	45.5	61.7
Aegean	54.2	102.7
Marmara	32.7	28.0
South East Anatolia	22.0	18.6
Black Sea	37.7	31.0
Average, all regions	25.8	36.3
Index	100	141

Source: For sources and details about these computations, see Appendix D, Table 1.

a. The averages for all regions in columns (1) and (2) were adjusted as the yields used to compute these figures are based on the data of the Central Statistical Office and should be too high for cereals. Without this adjustment the average for all regions in column (1) would be TL. 28.3, and in column (2) TL. 38.5.

decare) obtained for each of the four crops in
their respective regions, the effects of mechanization are abstracted from, and this difference
is due only to the fact that these farmers grew
more profitable crops. But note in Table 8 that
it is only on the average that these farmers receive the higher income per decare from their
four crops. In four regions out of six they actually have a lower income per decare. This is
rather puzzling. It not only contradicts what
one would expect on rational grounds; it seems
to contradict, too, the evidence of Table 7 which
shows that the farmers in the Mechanization
Study grew a greater proportion of the high-income industrial crops. How can one explain this?

A part of the reason for these unexpected
results is that in these calculations it has been
assumed that the large farmers grow only the four
main crops for which data are reported in the
Mechanization Study. Large farmers grow other
than the four crops, of course, and particularly
in the Black Sea region these other crops should
be very profitable. The figures in column (2)
of Table 8 for the Black Sea and possibly some
other regions are thus too small, although it is
not possible to estimate by how much.

Evidence from the Village Study suggests
still another reason why in Central Anatolia, and
probably in other regions where the main crops
give low incomes, the income per decare of small
farms may actually be higher than that of large
ones. Small farmers practice a much higher degree of self-sufficiency and therefore grow more
diversified crops than large ones.[14] While both
large and small farmers in Central Anatolia grow
wheat and barley predominantly, which give relatively low incomes per decare, the small farmers
grow relatively more fruits, vegetables, and
industrial crops whose income per decare is very
high, and these high-income crops more than compensate for the lower yields of the small farmers.[15] This is shown clearly in Table 9 (see

page 101). Column 5 of the table indicates that the largest farmers, although they operated land that, on the average, is twenty-two times as large as that of the farmers in the lowest bracket, use less than twenty-two times as much land for growing pulses and industrial crops, and use absolutely less land for vegetables and fruit gardens and for vineyards than do the smallest farmers. They use more than twenty-two times as much land only for cereals,[16] and column 6 shows that cereals provide less income per decare than most crops that small farmers grow in relatively larger amount.

In Central Anatolia, thus, the evidence from the Village Study supports the conclusion derived from Table 8 that the small farmers, because of differences in crops grown, actually derive a greater income per decare than the average farmer. The question should be raised, however, whether the higher yields of the small farmers are not at least partly illusory, a result of assigning the market price to crops like vegetables, which the smaller farmers grow in greater proportion. It seems most likely that, were a large enough market available to make it worthwhile for the large farmers to grow these crops in volume, the relationship would be reversed.

Summing up, differences due to the types of crops grown were found to make the distribution of gross income both more and less equal depending on the region, but in all regions combined, they make the distribution more unequal. The estimates showed that large farmers on the average derive 41 percent more gross income per decare than small ones, because they grow more lucrative crops. There is reason to believe, however, that this figure is too small, for the incomes of large farmers in the region of the Black Sea, if not some others, in this comparison are understated. Also, the value of the crops which small farmers grow in larger proportion are probably overstated for reasons shown.

TABLE 9

AMOUNT OF LAND (IN DECARES) SOWN TO DIFFERENT CROPS BY
FARMERS IN DIFFERENT LAND BRACKETS IN THE VILLAGE
STUDY,[a] AND AVERAGE GROSS INCOME PER DECARE
OF THESE CROPS

| | Farms by land-size brackets (in decares) | | | | Column (4) divided by column (1) | Average gross income per decare (in TL.)[b] |
	10-79 (1)	80-159 (2)	160-499 (3)	500 and over (4)	(5)	(6)
Average farm size	42.60	114.23	266.81	957.10	22	
Area planted to:						
Cereals	25.00	63.51	148.00	608.00	24	30
Pulses	1.00	1.32	3.21	2.85	3	18
Industrial crops	1.00	3.00	4.00	7.00	7	59
Vineyards	1.00	1.00	2.00	5.00	5	69
Fruit gardens	.10	1.00	.30	.05	0.5	111
Vegetable gardens	.20	1.00	.30	.20	1	55

a. Village Study, Table 3.

b. Computed from ibid., Tables 3, 5, 6, 10, 13, 14.

D. Differences Due to the Three Factors Combined

One can now evaluate the over-all extent to which the gross income per decare of the large farmers is likely to be greater than that of the small in the same province. It was found that mechanization increases yields by 39 percent. Since in the nation as a whole about 40 percent of the area of large farms is mechanized, mechanization should increase the yield of 40 percent of this area and give large farmers 16 percent higher incomes on that account (40 percent of 39 percent). The other factor that increased the gross incomes of the large farmers was the types of crops grown. It has been shown that this gave the mechanized farmers 41 percent higher incomes per decare and this percentage is taken to apply to large farmers generally. Methods of production other than mechanization had no significant effect. The combined effect of these two factors should give the large farmer 64 percent higher gross incomes per decare (116 percent of 141 percent).

Earlier in this chapter the distribution of gross crop incomes in Table 2 was shown to be more unequal than the distribution of land operated. Since the estimate in Table 2 rests on the assumption that within each province large and small farmers derive the same income per decare, at least so far as gross incomes are concerned, this assumption is not borne out, and the data in Table 2 greatly understate the degree of inequality in the distribution of gross incomes.

III. Second Approximation: The Distribution
of Gross Crop Incomes,
Including Differences in Gross
Incomes Between and Within Provinces

The estimates made in the preceeding
section enable one to adjust the first approximation of the distribution of gross crop incomes
in Table 2 (which only took account of differences in gross incomes per decare between provinces) to include the differences found in the
gross incomes per decare within provinces. To
do so it was first necessary to calculate to
what incomes in the first approximation of this
distribution the difference of 64 percent applied, and then to find by interpolation what
the difference would be for the other income
brackets in that distribution. In so doing it
has been assumed that the difference in the incomes per decare within provinces (of 64 percent) is evenly distributed among the income
brackets in the first approximation of the distribution, i.e., that the difference is proportionally smaller for farms whose incomes in
Table 2 are closer together, and greater for
those whose incomes are further apart than are
the incomes of the farms to which the 64 percent
difference applies.

The new distribution of gross incomes
which takes account of the differences in incomes
per decare both between and within provinces is
shown in Table 10 (see page 104).

TABLE 10

DISTRIBUTION OF GROSS CROP INCOMES, SECOND
APPROXIMATION: INCLUDING DIFFERENCES
IN GROSS CROP INCOMES BETWEEN
AND WITHIN PROVINCES[a]

Percent of all farm families	Percent of total gross crop income
Lowest 10%	.73
2nd lowest 10%	1.09
3rd lowest 10%	1.80
4th lowest 10%	2.57
5th lowest 10%	3.29
6th lowest 10%	4.40
7th lowest 10%	5.87
8th lowest 10%	8.02
9th lowest 10%	12.26
Highest 10%	59.98
	100%[b]

a. This distribution is derived from the first approximation distribution in Table 2 above by adjusting the
data in Table 2 to take account of the fact that within
provinces the gross incomes per decare of large farms
were found to be 64% higher than those of small ones.
This adjustment was made as follows:

The difference of 64% applied to farms of 7.2 hectares (the average size of all unmechanized farms) and
111.3 hectares (the average of all mechanized ones according to the Mechanization Study), and the gross
crop incomes in the first approximation distribution
of these two farm sizes is approximately TL. 2,000 and
TL. 31,000. (Calculated by multiplying 7.2 hectares

and 111.3 hectares by the average income per hectare of all farms in the first approximation distribution.)

To caclulate the second approximation distribution, incomes of TL. 31,000 in the first approximation distribution were raised 64%, while those of TL. 2,000 were left unchanged. The extent to which incomes of other sizes were raised or lowered was determined by interpolation. For example, an income half way between TL. 2,000 and TL. 31,000 in the first approximation distribution was raised 32% (half of 64%), or an income of TL. 60,000, which is twice as far removed from TL. 2,000 as TL. 31,000, was raised 128% (twice 64%). After these computations all incomes in the second approximation were adjusted so that their sum did not exceed the sum of all incomes in the first approximation distribution. (The actual incomes used for these computations were TL. 2,013 and TL. 31,119, rather than TL. 2,000 and TL. 31,000.)

b.   Percentages do not add up to 100 due to rounding.

CHAPTER VII

THE SHAPE OF THE DISTRIBUTION
OF NET CROP INCOMES

In talking of income distribution one has in mind the distribution of net and not gross incomes. In Chapter VI only gross incomes were considered. The next task, therefore, is to determine in what way considerations of costs might be expected to cause the distribution of net incomes to diverge from that of gross incomes derived above. The following are the basic points that arise in this regard:

1. Do the costs per decare of large farmers differ from those of the small because of differences in the relative amount of land that these farmers own and rent, and therefore of the amount of rent that they must pay?

2. Do the costs per decare of the large farmers differ from those of the small if the large farmers grow crops which yield a better gross income per decare? In other words, would costs cancel the difference bewteen the gross incomes per decare of the large and small farmer noted earlier, or would they cause even greater differences?

3. Aside from the possible differences in the costs of different crops, if large and small farmers grew the same crops would costs per decare of the large farmer generally be different from those of the small? One would expect that they would because on the one hand, large farmers should be more efficient and therefore save costs. On the other hand labor is an explicit cost for the large farmer but not for the small and in figuring net income only explicit costs should be taken account of. Thus with the possible exception of the mechanized farmer, a large farmer cannot cultivate all his fields himself, and therefore must pay out wages, an expense which the small farmer need not incur.

These three points cannot be neatly separated for reasons that will become evident, but
will be dealt with as the analysis proceeds.

A.   Costs of Large and Small Farmers in the
     Village Study

The only available source of statistics
on costs is the Village Study. To evaluate them
it was necessary to disentangle the share of animal costs that should be ascribed to work ani-
mals--a cost that should be attributed to crops--
and the costs incurred for non-work animals,
which do not help in raising crops. After this
adjustment was made (in Appendix A), the relative costs of large farmers were found to be
greater than those of small ones; small farmers
were left with 67 percent of their gross incomes
after costs were deducted, whereas large farmers
were left with only 48 percent.[1]
It is questionable, however, whether the
cost picture derived from the Village Study can
validly be generalized for all of Turkey. Why
this is so will be considered under the headings
of rents, labor costs, and other costs, in that
order.

(1) Representativeness of rents. The
large farmers in the Village Study spent more
than 100 times as much on rents as did the small
ones, although they operated only twenty-two
times as much land.[2] This would suggest that
the expenditures for rent are generally considerably higher for large than small farmers. But
the Village Study does not seem to be representative of the rental pattern in the country. As
far as the small farmers in this study are concerned, the average amount of land they rent seems
to be less than in the nation generally. Thus
full tenants--i.e., farmers who rent all the land
they operate--are likely to include only small
and medium size farmers, but not large ones,[3]
and in the Village Study only .5 percent of all

families were full renters,[4] whereas the average proportion in the nation was 3.8 percent.[5] Thus the number of small tenants and probably their expenditures for rents in the Village Study is less than appears to be the typical pattern in the nation.

One wonders why the Village Study sample included so few full tenants. One reason appears to be that the relative importance of full tenants in the regions surveyed in the Village Study is smaller than in the nation as a whole. According to the <u>1950 Agricultural Census Results</u>, the proportion in regions I and IX, which roughly correspond to the area included in the Village Study, is among the lowest of all regions in Turkey. This is shown in Table 1 (see page 109) where the regions are listed in order of increasing relative importance of tenancy conditions. In this table regions I and IX are the first and third from the top, i.e., among those with the lowest proportion of full tenants. The data in the table show that the national average is considerably affected by tenancy conditions prevailing in Eastern Turkey and the Mediterranean regions (the three regions on the bottom of the table), which together account for over half of all tenant families in the nation. Another very probable reason why full tenants in the Village Study are under-represented is that the Village Study sample includes too many large farmers and therefore gives the small and medium size farmers (including the full tenants among them) too small a chance to be included in the sample.[6]

One could roughly adjust the rents of small farmers in the Village Study by assuming that a larger number of full tenants would rent a proportionately greater amount of land. Since the proportion of full renters in the nation is seven times as large as it is in the Village Study,[7] the rents of full tenants among small farmers were increased seven-fold. A similar adjustment, based on the same assumptions, was made in the rents of the small Village Study

TABLE 1

REGIONAL DISTRIBUTION OF FULL TENANTS IN TURKEY AND THE
RELATIVE IMPORTANCE OF SUCH FAMILIES IN EACH REGION[a]

Region	Number of full tenants	Proportion of full tenants to all farm families in the region[b]
	(1)	(2)
Region I : Mid-North	3,587	1.0
" VII : Black Sea	3,946	1.0
" IX : Mid-South	3,733	1.7
" III : Marmara	4,947	2.4
" II : Aegean	14,960	3.9
" V : North-East	6,601	4.3
" VIII : Mid-East	11,503	5.5
" IV : Mediterranean	14,463	7.8
" VI : South-East	22,229	15.4
All regions	86,469	3.8

a. Calculated from 1950 Agricultural Census Results, p. 122.

b. Derived by taking the number of full tenants shown in
    column (1) as a proportion of the total number of farm
    families in each region. The total number of farm
    families in each region is shown in ibid., p. 122, but
    are not shown in this table.

farmers who are part-tenants, i.e., of families who rent only part of the land they operate. The proportion of part-tenants in the nation was found to be 1.26 times higher than it was in the Village Study,[8] and the rents of part-tenants were raised accordingly. As a result the average amount of rent paid by the small farmers in the Village Study was increased from TL. 23 to TL. 41.[9]

For the large farmers, too, the representativeness of the rents in the Village Study had to be examined. Among these farmers only those who are mechanized can be expected to rent land, and the degree of mechanization in a particular region is the major determinant of the average amount of land rented. But the proportion of additional land that is rented by mechanized farmers differs from region to region. Thus, the average large farmer in the Village Study may not be representative (1) because he is more or less mechanized than the average large farmer in the nation, and (2) because in Central Anatolia generally mechanized farmers rent more or less land than does the average mechanized farmer in the nation.

The extent to which the large farms in the Village Study are more or less mechanized than the average large farm in the nation can be gauged approximately by using the ratio of "area operated" to "tractors owned" by large farmers as a measure of the degree of mechanization. This ratio turned out to be almost identical when it was computed for all farms with over 500 decares in the nation and for those of corresponding size in the Village Study[10] indicating that the large farms in the Village Study are just about as mechanized as the large farms generally. Assuming from (1) above that the amount of land large farmers rent varies with the degree of mechanization, the large farmers in the Village Study should rent, on the average, about the same amount of land as large farmers do in the nation, all other things being equal.

But as noted in (2) above, the amount of land the mechanized farmers rent differs from region to region. In the Village Study it is about 44 percent of the area operated,[11] which is very close to the average of 46 percent for Central Anatolia found in the Mechanization Study.[12] But according to this latter study it is only 30 percent for the nation as a whole.[13] On this account one would therefore expect that the typical large farmer in the Village Study would rent about 150 percent as much land as does the typical large farmer in the nation. Since the difference in the degree of mechanization was found to be negligible the rents of the large Village Study farmer had to be adjusted only for the extent to which these farmers rent more land than large farmers do generally (150 percent of the average). Therefore the rents of the large farmers in the Village Study were reduced by one third (equivalent to division by 1.5) to make them representative of all large farmers in the nation.

After the rent data in the Village Study were adjusted for the estimated understatement of land rents of the small farmer and the over-statement of those of the large ones, rent as a proportion of all crop costs was found to be 13 percent for small farmers and 18 percent for large ones.[14] This changed the ratio of crop costs to gross crop income in the Village Study from 33 percent to 35 percent for the lowest land bracket, and from 52 percent to 48 percent for the highest.[15]

(2) <u>Representativeness of labor costs</u>. The next question considered was whether the labor costs in the Village Study were any more representative for the country generally than the rent figures. To analyze these data average labor costs were divided by average farm size for each land bracket.[16] The resulting labor costs per decare appeared questionable at first glance, as they were smaller for the highest land bracket

than for any of the others. Since these costs
include only paid and not family labor, and
large farmers should require more outside help,
one might have expected the opposite relationship. Reflection suggests, however, that this
relationship makes sense. The large farmers in
the Village Study needed less labor because they
were fairly mechanized, as tractors are labor-
saving equipment. To what extent their labor
costs were representative for Turkey generally
thus depends on whether the degree of mechanization of large farmers in the Village Study was
the same as that for large farmers in other re-
fions. Earlier the difference had been found to
be negligible so that on that account these labor
costs should be representative.

(3) Representativeness of other costs.
There still remain costs other than rents and
wages, and here, too, it is necessary to investi-
gate how representative the data in the Village
Study are for Turkey generally.

Table 2 (see page 113) shows that much of
these other costs of large farmers consists of
such items as expenses for fuel (line 5), repair
and depreciation of machinery (line 4) and rent
of machines (line 6). Together these amount to
more than one third of total expenses of large
farmers other than land rents. The table also
shows that these costs are largely compensated
for by other costs which do not increase in proportion to the greater amount of land operated
by large farmers.

Thus, while the area operated by the
farmers in the largest land bracket was twenty-
two times as great as that of farmers in the
smallest bracket (line 1), the large farmer
spent less than twenty-two times as much on labor (line 2), depreciation and repair of buildings (line 11), small tools (such as hoes, harnesses, horseshoes, etc.), called "other" in
Table 2, and shown in line 12, feed (line 10),

TABLE 2

CROP COSTS OF LARGE AND SMALL FARMERS IN THE VILLAGE
STUDY COMPARED[a]

		Lowest land bracket (1)	Highest land bracket (2)	Column (2) divided by column (1) (3)
1.	Amount of land operated (decares)[b]	42.60	957.10	22
2.	Cost of hired labor (TL.)	42	869	21
3.	Cost of seed bought and produced on the farm (TL.)	124	2,696	22
4.	Expenditures on equipment (depreciation, repairs, and spare parts) (TL.)	22	1,775	81
5.	Fuel costs (TL.)	-	1,293	infinity
6.	Rent of machinery (TL.)	3	425	142
7.	Taxes (TL.)	14	93	7
8.	Interest on debts (TL.)	29	509	18
9.	Fertilizer (TL.)	2	50	25
10.	Feed (TL.)	24	25	1
11.	Depreciation and repair of buildings (TL.)	29	116	4
12.	Other (TL.)	24	324	10
13.	Total cost except land rent (TL.)	323	8,175	25
14.	Total cost, except land rent, per decare[c] (TL.)	7.58	8.54	1.13
15.	Land rent (as shown in the Village Study) (TL.)	23	2,598	113
16.	Land rent in the Village Study adjusted to make it representative for the country as a whole	41[d]	1,732[e]	42

a. Appendix A, Table 2, except where otherwise indicated.

b. Village Study, Table 1.

c. Line 13 divided by line 1.

d. To adjust the Village Study figure in line 15, the portion of this rent paid by full tenants was increased seven-fold, and the portion paid by part-tenants by 26%, as explained in part A(1) of this chapter.

e. Adjusted by reducing the rent figure in line 15 by one-third. (See part A(1) of this chapter.)

and a number of other items. This indicates that
the expense of machinery saves not only labor,
but some other costs as well, and that there are
in addition some economies of scale. Although
mechanization entails additional costs, it also
creates savings and these savings are large
enough to make the difference between the costs
per decare (other than land rent) of the large
and small farmers (line 14) relatively small.
Since earlier in this chapter it was found that
the degree to which the large farmers in the
Village Study are mechanized seems to be representative for large farmers in the nation, and
since the pattern of costs discussed depends
largely on size of farm and degree of mechanization, the "other costs" in the Village Study
should also, on the whole, be representative.

Analysis of the costs of large and small
farmers in the Village Study also reveals some
important aspects of the differences and similar-
ities in methods of production practiced by these
farmers. In Chapter I it had been shown that to
increase agricultural output in the nation the
basic needs of Turkish agriculture consist of
additional draft power (tractors), as well as
irrigation and fertilizer. The extent to which
tractors increase yields and the degree to which
large farmers are mechanized was discussed in
Chapter VI. Insofar as they are mechanized,
large farmers have contributed to the increased
crop output of the nation and at the same time
have made very handsome profits on the equipment
purchased.[17] But the Village Study also shows
that the large farmers spend no more per decare
on fertilizer (Table 2, line 9), and irrigated
the same negligible portion of their land as the
small farmers.[18] These data support the conclusion arrived at earlier that, aside from
mechanization, large farmers do not use any better methods of production than small ones.

At the outset of this chapter three major
factors making for differences in costs of farms
of different sizes were noted. These were dif-

ferences due to (1) differences in the amount of rent paid, (2) differences in types of crops grown which could entail different costs, and (3) differences in methods of production. The Village Study was found to be representative for (3), and could be adjusted for (1). Why (2) has not yet been considered is explained in the next section. Assuming for the moment that the conditions mentioned in (2) are neutral, the ratios of crop costs (with rents adjusted) to gross crop incomes of 35 percent for small farmers and 48 percent for large ones, which had been calculated earlier from the Village Study data, will be accepted provisionally as the cost ratios that apply to farms of different sizes.

These costs were incorporated into the distribution of gross crop incomes derived in Chapter VI (Table 10) by linear interpolation, and the resulting distribution of net incomes is presented in Table 3 (see page 117). This distribution was derived by first determining to what income levels in the distribution of gross incomes the incomes of the large and small farmers in the Village Study corresponded; the corresponding incomes were reduced 48 percent and 35 percent respectively; for other income levels costs were taken to be 1 percent higher or lower than 35 percent for each 1/13 (or $\frac{1}{48-35}$) increase or decrease in income in the distribution of gross incomes away from the income to which the 35 percent cost ratio applied.

B. Differences in Costs When Large and Small Farmers Grow Different Crops

To some extent the large and small farmers included in the Village Study grow different crops. In the analysis made above this factor was considered since the costs included all crops grown by the farmers in the study. However, among these farmers wheat and barley are such a large proportion of the total crop[19] that dif-

TABLE 3

DISTRIBUTION OF NET CROP INCOMES[a]

Percent of all farm families	Percent of total net crop income
Lowest 10%	.79
2nd lowest 10%	1.19
3rd lowest 10%	1.95
4th lowest 10%	2.78
5th lowest 10%	3.56
6th lowest 10%	4.74
7th lowest 10%	6.29
8th lowest 10%	8.54
9th lowest 10%	12.89
Highest 10%	57.26
	100.00

a. The differences in costs of 35% and 48% applied to
    the gross income levels in the distribution of gross
    crop incomes (in Chapter VI, Table 10) of the farmers
    in the lowest and highest land brackets in the Village
    Study of TL. 1,037 and TL. 20,783. These incomes were
    reduced by 35% and 48%. The cost reductions applied
    to other income levels were found by linear interpola-
    tion, as explained in the text.

ferences in costs of large and small farmers in
the Village Study should not be very much affected by the fact that they also grow different
crops. Most of the costs are wheat and barley
costs for farmers of all sizes. In the nation
as a whole, however, large and small farmers do
not grow the same crops to the same extent as
they do in Central Anatolia, so that the cost
data in the Village Study shed only very little
light on this aspect of the question.

Unfortunately, data on the costs of different crops are not available. Analysis, however, suggests that the better crops yield not
only a higher gross, but also a higher net income and that this factor tends to make the distribution more unequal than that shown in Table
3. There are several reasons for this.

For one, crops like wheat and barley,
which yield a relatively low income per decare,
are grown both in the provinces in which the average income per decare is low and in those in
which it is high.[20] In the latter areas, the
large farmers grew relatively more of the better
income crops and the small farmers relatively
more cereals, and this, as was shown above, was
one of the reasons why the large farmers obtained
considerably higher incomes per decare than the
average in their provinces. But the large
farmer could also grow more cereals, just as the
small farmer does. Whether or not he does so
depends, of course, on his motives for choosing
different crops, and on his knowledge of the con-
sequences of alternative choices. Since the
large farmer is also a commercial farmer, he can
be expected to follow his profit motive at least
in the choice of crops produced for sale. If he
is aware of other crops that could be grown in
his area, and is informed about both costs and
prices, he would choose to grow crops that yield
a higher gross return only when they also yield
a higher net return or profit. But this raises
the question why the small farmer should follow

his money advantage less than the large one. The answer is evident.

The small farmer is largely self-sufficient. This is shown in the Village Study if one bears in mind the unusually good crop year during which the study was conducted and the fact that it was itself preceeded by two other good crop years. Thus, according to the study, the farmers in the lowest land bracket sold 31 percent of their gross crop output.[21] But since 1953, the year to which the data in the Village Study refer, was the best crop year that is remembered in the history of Turkish agriculture,[22] a far greater surplus should have been left for sale than during a more normal year, and since the two previous years were also good,[23] little of this surplus should have been needed to replenish the stocks that farmers typically keep on hand as a precautionary measure in the event of poor years. In more normal years, therefore, these same farmers should have had little, if anything, for sale.

If the small farmer consumes most of his output, the dominant consideration in his choice among alternate crops should be his need for home consumption, while for the large farmer who produces primarily for the market, the choice of crops should be determined by his expected net sales income. Therefore, the large farmer can be expected to grow crops that, to his knowledge, produce the highest net income per decare, while the small farmer would do so only when the hierarchy of market valuation coincides with that of his own needs.[24] Since large farmers do not generally know less about growing conditions, costs, and prices, than small farmers, it is difficult to conceive of a situation where the commercial farmer would choose to grow crops different from those of the small farmer if he did not expect them to increase his net income. Of course, price declines can upset expectations in a particular area and in a particular year, but these observations should apply in the av-

erage case, if one generalizes about the behavior
of commercial farmers in all high-income provinces. Thus the higher gross incomes of the
large farmers in the better regions should also
mean higher net incomes.

Would these net incomes be higher to a
greater or lesser extent than the gross incomes?
Only if costs are more than proportionally greater for the crops with higher gross incomes will
net incomes be more equal, e.g., if one crop
yields twice as much gross income as another at
twice the cost, the net income derived from the
first crop bears the same relation to the second,
2:1, as do their gross incomes. It is generally
believed that for most part the costs of high-
income crops, though greater than for low-income
crops, are not proportionally greater. It follows from this that there should be an even
greater relative difference in net return between good and bad crops than in gross return.
Were precise data available it would be desirable to adjust for this difference. Such data,
however, do not exist, so that all one can do is
suggest that the distribution shown in Table 3
understates the degree of inequality in net income.

CHAPTER VIII

THE SHAPE OF THE DISTRIBUTION OF
NET CROP AND ANIMAL INCOMES

The distributions of income that were derived
in Chapter VI for gross crop incomes, and in
Chapter VII for net crop incomes, are based on
the distribution of land operated individually
by farm families. However, animals, though individually owned, are grazed on common land, so
that the income that families derive from their
animals bears little relation to the size of the
land they operate. The total amount of income
from animals is very large. According to the
official data it amounts to 35 percent of the
total gross agricultural incomes (crop and animal).[1] Although it has been shown that these incomes are overstated in the official data, there
is no doubt that they supplement crop incomes to
a significant degree. The next problems are
therefore to find a way of determining how animal
incomes are distributed, and to combine this distribution with that of crop incomes. These two
problems will be dealt with jointly.

The method used for estimating the distribution of crop and animal incomes is essentially
the same as that which had been used for deriving
the distribution of crop incomes alone, and for
lack of any data that would enable a more direct
approach, it, too, takes the distribution of land
operated as a point of departure.

Since animal incomes are not obviously
related to (crop) land operated, the logic of
deriving the distribution of animal incomes from
that of land operated requires clarification.
Basic to the estimate of the distribution of
crop incomes had been the consideration that the
distributions of income and of land operated would
exhibit identical degrees of inequality only if
incomes were strictly proportional to size of

farm, in other words, if all farmers received
the same income per decare of land operated.
Therefore the modifications made in the distribution of land operated in the previous chapters
attempted to take into account the factors that
would cause crop incomes per decare of land operated to vary for different farms.

The same consideration could also be applied to animal incomes. The distribution of animal incomes and of land operated would be identical in degree of inequality if animal incomes
were distributed in proportion to land operated,
or if, per decare of land operated, all farms received the same income from animals. It follows
from this that the difference between the degree
of inequality of these two distributions could
be estimated if the factors that cause animal incomes per decare of land operated to differ for
different farms could be determined, and if their
effect coujld be measured.[2]

The following factors would cause animal
incomes not to be proportional to amount of land
operated:

1. Differences in animal incomes per decare of land operated between provinces. These
are caused by variations, from province to province, in the amount and quality of pasture land
relative to the amount of (crop) land operated,
and result in provincial variations in number,
types, and quality of animals pastured, and therefore in the income derived from animals in relation to each decare of land operated.

2. Differences in animal incomes per decare of land operated within each province, caused
by the fact that the animal incomes of farms of
different sizes are not necessarily proportional
to size of land operated.

3. Differences in animal costs in relation to farm size.

These three factors are the same in type
as those that caused the distribution of crop incomes to differ from that of land operated--

Chapters VI and VII were devoted to estimating the magnitude of their effects for the distribution of crop and animal incomes combined. The steps in the method are the same as those used earlier: First the distribution of land operated is modified to take into account variations in crop and animal incomes per decare between provinces; within each province it is assumed provisionally that these incomes are distributed in proportion to size of farm, or that they are equal, per decare of land operated, for farms of all sizes. Next the assumption of equal incomes per decare of large and small farms within provinces is relaxed, and the previous distribution is modified for the effect of these differences. The third adjustment takes into account the extent to which costs of both crops and stock raising differ for large and small farmers.

A. Firts Approximation: The Distribution of Gross Crop and Animal Incomes, Assuming Equal Incomes per Decare Within Provinces

The distribution of gross incomes in Chapter VI is recalculated to include animal incomes (as well as crop incomes) and is shown in Table 1 (see page 124). To calculate this distribution, the assumption is made that both crop and animal incomes are distributed in each province exactly as the distribution of land operated. Thus the data in Table 1 differ from the distribution of land operated only because of the differences in animal and crop incomes between provinces. When this new distribution is compared with that of gross crop incomes (also shown in Table 1), it is seen that the addition of animal incomes makes the overall distribution more equal than the distribution of crop incomes alone, at least in their first approximation.

TABLE 1

DISTRIBUTION OF GROSS CROP AND ANIMAL INCOMES, OF GROSS CROP INCOMES ALONE,
AND OF GROSS ANIMAL INCOMES DERIVED BY SUBTRACTION. FIRST
APPROXIMATION: ASSUMING THAT WITHIN PROVINCES THESE
INCOMES ARE DISTRIBUTED IN PROPORTION TO THE
DISTRIBUTION OF LAND OPERATED

Percent of all families	Distribution of gross crop and animal incomes[a]		Distribution of gross crop incomes[b]		Distribution of gross animal incomes[c]	
	000,000 TL.	% of total	000,000 TL.	% of total	000,000 TL.	% of total
(1)	(2)	(3)	(4)	(5)	(6)	(7)
Lowest 10%	95.6	1.00	53.6	0.86	42.0	1.24
2nd lowest 10%	137.0	1.43	79.9	1.29	57.2	1.69
3rd lowest 10%	210.0	2.19	131.1	2.11	78.9	2.33
4th lowest 10%	296.0	3.09	186.0	3.00	110.0	3.25
5th lowest 10%	396.3	4.13	238.1	3.83	158.2	4.67
6th lowest 10%	518.0	5.40	315.4	5.08	202.6	5.98
7th lowest 10%	658.3	6.86	417.3	6.72	241.0	7.11
8th lowest 10%	887.8	9.25	562.6	9.06	325.3	9.60
9th lowest 10%	1,310.0	13.65	840.2	13.53	469.5	13.86
Highest 10%	5,088.8	53.02	3,385.3	54.51	1,703.6	50.28
Total[d]	9,597.5	100.00[e]	6,209.5	100.00[e]	3,388.0	100.00[e]

Mean income (in TL.)			
True mean[d]	3,273	2,122	1,151
Mean calculated from the above distribution[d]	3,797	2,456	1,340
Median income (TL.)	1,758	1,006	749

a. The distribution of gross crop and animal incomes in columns (2) and (3) was computed by the same method and from the same sources as that derived for gross crop incomes alone in columns (4) and (5). Details of the method and the sources used are shown in note a to Table 2 of Cahpter VI, if one substitutes the words "gross crop and animal incomes" for the words "gross crop incomes" whenever they occur in that note.

b. This distribution is the same as that shown in Chapter VI, Table 2.

c. To derive the animal incomes in column (6), the gross crop incomes in column (4) were subtracted from the gross crop and animal incomes in column (2). In column (7) the animal incomes in column (6) were converted into a percent distribution.

d. The total income derived in these calculations is larger than the actual total gross crop or gross animal income shown in Türkiye Zirai İstihsal Kıymeti 1952. This is due to the fact that the distribution of land operated upon which the distributions in this table are based seems to list relatively too many medium size farms in the better crop areas, while at the same time understating the number of large farms in these better crop areas. On balance the understatement of the medium size farms seems to more than compensate for the overstatement of the large farms in these better areas, and therefore gives rise to too large a total income in the distributions we have calculated. For details of these over and understatements see Appendix E. These overstatements are apart from any overstatements estimated in the official data. Those mentioned here only arose in the course of our manipulation of the official data.

e. Percentages may not add up to 100 due to rounding.

B. The Distribution of Gross Animal Incomes
    Within Provinces

      The next question that needs to be con-
sidered is: How would the distribution of animal incomes within provinces modify the results
shown in our first approximation in Table 1?
      The scanty data available indicate that
the distribution would become still more equal.
These are the data shown in the Village Study
(see Table 2, page 127), and they indicate that
for the farmers sampled in this study, on the
average, the greater the amount of land a farmer
operates, the smaller is the proportion of both
his investment and income from animals in relation to the size of his land. While families in
the largest land bracket in the Village Study
operated twenty-two times as much land as the
smallest, they had only six times as large an
investment in non-work animals. Although their
rate of return from these animals was slightly
higher than for the small farmer, their total
income from animals was still only eight times
greater. The data in the Village Study therefore suggest that animal income is an equalizing
factor of significant magnitude in the distribution of gross agricultural incomes. This is not
only suggested by the scanty data, it is the
generally held view of those most familiar with
Turkish agriculture.
      To what extent, then, do animal incomes
equalize the overall distribution of net incomes?
In order to answer the question it is necessary
first to consider how costs incurred in raising
animals affect the distribution of gross incomes,
i.e., how the distribution of net incomes would
differ from that of gross incomes derived above.

C. The Distribution of Net Animal Incomes
    Within Provinces

      The data in the Village Study indicate
that net incomes from animals are not distribu-

TABLE 2

GROSS INCOME AND INVESTMENT IN NON-WORK ANIMALS IN
RELATION TO SIZE OF FARMS IN THE VILLAGE STUDY

| | Farms by land-size brackets (in decares) | | | |
	10-79 (1)	80-159 (2)	160-499 (3)	500 and over (4)
Average amount of land operated				
1. In decares[a]	42.60	114.23	266.81	957.10
2. Index, column (1) = 1.00	1.00	2.68	6.26	22.47
Gross income from animals				
3. In TL.[b]	311	510	986	2,501
4. Index, column (1) = 1.00	1.00	1.64	3.17	8.04
Value of non-work animals				
5. In TL.[c]	710	1,028	2,025	4,524
6. Index, column (1) = 1.00	1.00	1.45	2.85	6.38

a. Village Study, Table 28.

b. Ibid., Table 2.

c. The value of work animals and non-work animals is not given separately in the Village Study and had to be estimated. See Appendix A, Table 3.

127

ted very differently from gross. The main reason for expecting any difference would be labor costs, i.e., if small farmers do not hire the services of paid shepherds while large ones do. But according to the Village Study, 68 percent of the small farmers and 75 percent of the large farmers hired shepherds, and since shepherd wages constitute only a small portion of the gross income from non-work animals the cost differences become negligible. Table 3 (see page 129) shows the cost ratios for animals and animal products and the gross and net incomes from non-work animals which are estimated from the data in the Village Study. Although the cost ratios of the large farmers are somewhat higher than those of the small (Table 3, line 7), the large farmers also earn somewhat higher gross incomes from animals in relation to their investment in them than small farmers (compare in Table 2, lines 4 and 6), so that the net incomes of the two groups differ about as much as the gross incomes (Table 3, lines 2 and 6).

D. Second Approximation: The Distribution of Net Crop and Animal Income, Taking Account of Differences in Incomes Between and Within Provinces and in Costs

How much animal incomes equalize the over-all distribution of net incomes is difficult to determine from the available data. All one can do is assume that net animal incomes are distributed within provinces as they are in the Village Study and try to determine to what extent, within provinces, the equalizing effect of the distribution of animal incomes is counterbalanced by the unequalizing effect of the distribution of crop incomes, analyzed in Chapters VI and VII.[3] This leaves open the question, of course, as to how representative the distribution of animal incomes in the Village Study is for Turkey as a whole, a question which will be considered in turn.

TABLE 3

AVERAGE GROSS AND NET ANIMAL INCOMES PER LAND
BRACKET IN THE VILLAGE STUDY[a]
(In TL.)

	Farms by land-size brackets (in decares)			
	10-79	80-159	160-499	500 and over
	(1)	(2)	(3)	(4)
1. Gross animal incomes (TL.)	311	510	986	2,501
2. Index, column (1) = 1.00	1.00	1.64	3.17	8.04
3. Cost of non-work animals (TL.)	53	122	211	585
4. Index, column (1) = 1.00	1.00	2.30	3.98	11.04
5. Net animal incomes	258	388	775	1,916
6. Index, column (1) = 1.00	1.00	1.50	3.00	7.43
7. Cost as % of gross incomes[b]	17%	24%	21%	23%

a. See Appendix A, Table 3.

b. Line (3) as % of line (1).

129

Assuming then that net animal incomes within provinces are distributed as they are in the Village Study, the difference, within provinces, of net crop and animal incomes per decare has been estimated, and the combined results then used to modify the distribution of gross crop and animal incomes in Table 1, which only takes account of differences in gross incomes between provinces. For the "within provinces" estimate, the Village Study data served as a point of departure, but were modified so that they could be generalized to all provinces in the nation. To do so the large farms in the Village Study were assigned a higher gross crop income per decare than small ones since it had been found previously that gross crop incomes within provinces are higher for large farmers. Moreover, since the average income per decare in the Village Study is lower than the average in the nation, the average of both large and small farmers was raised so as to be representative of all regions. For gross animal incomes the farmers in the Village Study were assigned an income per decare of land cultivated that, on the average, is equal to the average in the nation (rather than the average in the Village Study, since the average in the nation is considerably higher), but that is distributed between large and small farmers as animal incomes are distributed in the Village Study. From these incomes costs had to be subtracted; and the costs used were the percentages of gross income which had been computed for large and small farmers in the Village Study for crops in Chapter VII, and for animals in Table 3 of this chapter. The estimate of the degree to which the differences in net crop and animal incomes within provinces might offset one another is presented in Table 4 (see page 131). As shown in the table, the computations indicate that net crop and animal incomes per decare of land for small farmers are 23 percent greater than those of large farmers. Therefore it appears that within provinces

TABLE 4

ESTIMATE OF THE DIFFERENCE IN NET CROP AND ANIMAL INCOMES
PER DECARE OF LARGE AND SMALL FARMERS WITHIN PROVINCES

		Small farms	Large farms
		(1)	(2)
1.	Gross crop incomes per decare (TL.)[a]	27.45	43.18
2.	Crop costs per decare (TL.)[b]	-9.63	-20.70
3.	Net crop incomes per decare (TL.)	17.82	22.58
4.	Gross animal income per decare (TL.)[c]	20.29	7.26
5.	Animal costs per decare (TL.)[d]	-3.45	- 1.70
6.	Net animal income per decare (TL.)	16.84	5.56
7.	Net crop and animal income per decare (TL.)	34.66	28.14
8.	Index of line 7, large farms = 100	123	100
9.	Gross animal incomes per decare as percent of gross crop and animal incomes per decare	43	14
10.	Net animal incomes per decare as percent of net crop and animal incomes per decare	49	20

a. The gross crop incomes were calculated in two steps:
(1) The difference of 64% in the gross crop incomes per
decare of large and small farmers within provinces
which had been derived in Chapter VI, had to be made

to apply to the same farm sizes as do all other data in this table. All others were derived directly from the Village Study and therefore pertain to the average farm sizes of the lowest and highest land brackets of 43 and 957 decares in that study. However, in note a to Table 10 of Chapter VI, the difference of 64% was shown to apply to farms of 72 and 1113 decares respectively. The difference was therefore interpolated to apply to farms of 43 and 957 decares. (This was done by the method explained in the note to the table just referred to.) (2) The results in (1) were then converted into percents of the gross crop income per decare of farms of average size in the nation of TL. 28 (computed from Türkiye Zirai Kıymeti 1952, p. 4, and Monthly Bulletin of Statistics, No. 34-36, p. 169); the small farms in the Village Study were found to receive 99% of this income, and the large ones 143%. Therefore the average gross income of TL. 28 was multiplied by these percentages. The results, shown in line 1 of this table, should represent the average gross crop incomes per decare in the nation of farms of the size of the small and large ones in the Village Study.

b. Calculated on the assumption that the ratio of gross crop costs to gross crop incomes in the nation is the same as the ratio calculated for small and large farmers in the Village Study of 35 and 48%.

c. The gross animal incomes per decare assigned to these farms were derived from Appendix A, Table 3. These figures were then increased 2.78 times, since in the nation as a whole animal incomes in the official data are that much more important than they are in the Village Study. The figure of 2.78 was derived by dividing the average animal income per decare of land cultivated in the nation of TL. 15.25 (computed from the identical page number references and publications mentioned in note a) by the corresponding figure of TL. 5.48 for the Village Study (computed from Appendix A, Table 3, and Table 2 of this chapter).

d. The animal costs per decare are those of large and small farmers in the Village Study (computed from Appendix A, Table 3, and Table 2 of this chapter), except that they were increased 2.78 times, just as the gross animal incomes.

the greater equality of animal incomes more than compensates for the greater inequality of crop incomes.

These figures were used to revise the first approximation of the over-all distribution of gross crop and animal incomes in Table 1. This was done by applying the difference of 23 percent to farms of the average sizes of large and small farms in the Village Study, or rather to the average income in the nation that would correspond to farms of these sizes, and by assuming for farms of different sizes that this difference is proportional to size of farm. For example, a farm with a size halfway between the large and small farms in the Village Study would be assigned an income that is 11.5 percent higher than that of the large farms. The new distribution based upon this adjustment is shown in Table 5 (see page 134).

The distribution in Table 5, as noted, rests in part on the estimates made in Table 4, which in turn are based on two main assumptions: (1) that animal incomes within provinces are distributed in the nation as they were in the Village Study and (2) that the relative importance of crop and animal incomes in the nation is correctly represented by the official data. The accuracy of the official data has already been questioned. One figure in Table 4 leads one to question it again, and therefore to question the distribution derived in Table 5. For as shown in Table 4 (lines 9 and 10), nearly one half of the small farmer's gross income is taken to derive from animals, and almost exactly one half of his net income, a situation that seems implausible. Why were these implausible results derived? They followed from the assumption that crop and animal incomes are distributed in the country as they are in the Village Study coupled with the fact that on the average crop incomes per decare in the nation are about one fourth higher than they are in the Village Study[4] while animal incomes per decare in the

TABLE 5

DISTRIBUTION OF NET CROP AND ANIMAL INCOMES ESTIMATED ON
THE ASSUMPTION THAT ANIMAL INCOMES WITHIN PROVINCES
ARE DISTRIBUTED AS THEY ARE IN THE VILLAGE STUDY
AND THAT THE RELATIVE IMPORTANCE OF CROP
AND ANIMAL INCOMES IS THAT SHOWN
IN THE OFFICIAL DATA[a]

Percent of all farm families	Percent of total agricultural incomes
Lowest 10%	1.06
2nd lowest 10%	1.51
3rd lowest 10%	2.31
4th lowest 10%	3.25
5th lowest 10%	4.35
6th lowest 10%	5.67
7th lowest 10%	7.19
8th lowest 10%	9.65
9th lowest 10%	14.12
Highest 10%	50.89
	100%

a. This distribution has been derived from the distribu-
    tion of gross crop and animal incomes in Table 1 (which
    takes account of differences in incomes between pro-
    vinces) by applying to it the differences within pro-
    vinces in the net crop and animal incomes of large and
    small farmers derived in Table 4. These two tables
    were combined in the following manner: The difference
    of 23% in the net crop and animal incomes in Table 4
    applies to farms of the sizes of the largest and smal-
    lest land brackets in the Village Study of 957 and 43
    decares. If one generalizes this difference to farms

of these sizes in the nation as a whole, it would apply to farms with total gross incomes from crops and
animals of TL. 1,841 and TL. 41,356 (derived by multiplying these land sizes by the average gross crop and
animal income per decare in the nation of TL. 43.21
(see notes a and c to Table 4 above). To incorporate
this difference into the distribution in Table 1, incomes of TL. 1,841 in this distribution were raised
23% and those of TL. 41,346 were left unchanged. For
other income levels the difference was determined by
linear interpolation. (For details of the method used,
see Chapter VI, Table 10, note a.) In the end the
total incomes of each tenth of farm families were adjusted for the fact that the changes made caused the
sum of the percentages to be greater than 100%.

nation, according to the official data, are
nearly three times as large. (See notes c and d
in Table 4.)   In the Village Study the small
farmers derive only 26 percent of their gross and
27 percent of their net agricultural incomes from
animals.[5] But to make the Village Study data
representative for the nation as a whole the
Village Study animal incomes per decare in Table
4 were raised nearly threefold (but the crop incomes per decare only one fourth).   Thus in the
distribution in Table 4, as shown in lines 9 and
10, the small farmer gets 43 percent of his total
gross income from animals, and nearly half (49
percent) of his total net income.

It is questionable that a distribution
in which small farmers derive half of their incomes from animals is representative.   In earlier
discussions of the animal incomes in the official
data it was noted that these overstate their
value.   The following data on comsumption raise
further doubts about the relative importance of
crop and animal incomes in the official data.
The doubts arise because one would expect that
there would be some relation between the proportion of animal income produced and consumed for,
if animal products are so important in the output
of small farmers, they should be at least fairly
important in their consumption.   Thus, the Village Study shows that for the small farmer animal
products constitute one fourth of the value of
home-produced consumption and about the same
ratio of the value of agricultural output.[6] The
little evidence available on consumption of animal
products by small farmers indicates that it is no
more important in other regions than it is in the
Village Study.   A Konjonktür survey done on the
expenditures of Turkish farmers in 1935-1936 in
five regions shows that in all these regions animal products constituted no more than one fourth
of the value of food consumed.[7] The Konjonktür
survey apparently represents the average farmer.
But for Central Anatolia more detailed statistics
are also available for farms of different sizes,

and these indicate that the small farmer (whose
total gross income was less than half the average
in the region), consumed about the same percentage of animal products as the large one and that
the regional average seemed to represent the small
farmer fairly well in this respect.[8]

It should be added that the relative income level of the small farmers in the Konjonktür
survey was considerably lower than that of the
small farmers in the Village Study.[9] Since animal incomes appear to have an equalizing effect
on income distribution, so that the share of the
total income derived from animal products should
be relatively larger for farmers with lower incomes, the consumption pattern in the Konjonktür
survey suggests even more strongly than the Village Study that the distribution in Table 5 overstates the relative importance of animal products
of small farmers.

Of course, production and consumption of
animal products do not necessarily constitute
identical ratios of total production. But insofar as there is some relation, as one imagines
there would be, and as was also shown for the
Village Study where the ratios are very similar,[10] the analysis suggests that the figures in
Table 5 overstate the equalizing effect of animal
incomes.

It should be added that the evidence on
the consumption of animal products that has been
cited applies only to regions in which crop incomes are the chief source of agricultural incomes.
Neither the Village Study, nor the regions that
form part of the Konjonktür survey include any
of the eastern provinces in many of which, contrary to most western provinces, animal incomes
constitute the greater part of total agricultural income. One wonders whether in these provinces the consumption of animal products by
small farmers may not be considerably greater
than in the predominantly crop areas and thus
significantly affect the average for the nation.
But it is clear that they do not; the total out-

put of these provinces is not sufficiently important to affect the national average to any significant degree. The ratio of gross animal incomes to total gross agricultural incomes is only slightly higher when the Eastern regions (agricultural regions V and VI) are included than when they were excluded.[11] Nor could the results be affected in any significant way by the nomads who derive all their income from animals and none from crops. According to the available data the number of "livestock only" families are too small to be of any significance.[12]

It is clear therefore that the distribution in Table 5 overstates the degree of equality of animal and crop incomes, but it is impossible to estimate the extent to which this is so. Since the data are so scanty all that can be done is to interpret this distribution as the probable lower limit to the degree of inequality that exists in the distribution of agricultural incomes in Turkey. By a method similar to the one used for deriving this lower limit distribution, it is possible to derive a distribution that should set the upper limit to the degree of inequality of agricultural incomes. Since the income from animals apparently has some equalizing effect on income distribution within provinces (because ownership of animals seems to be distributed less unequally than size of land operated), a distribution in which it is assumed that within provinces animal incomes are distributed in proportion to land operated should result in too much inequality. To derive this distribution, the difference, per decare, in net crop and animal incomes within provinces, which had been estimated in Table 4 for the lower limit distribution, was recalculated, after assigning to large and small farmers the same gross and net animal incomes per decare. (The gross and net crop incomes per decare, which in Table 4 are higher for large than small farmers were, of course, left unchanged in these recomputations.)

The lower and upper limit distributions (the latter new) are shown in columns (1) and (2) in Table 6 (see page 140) to enable comparison.

It is surprising that these two distributions do not differ as much as might be expected. In the former the highest tenth receives 51 percent of the total income and in the latter 55 percent, a difference of four percentage points. Since the difference is not too large and since, moreover, the one distribution shows almost certainly too much equality of income and the other too little, the two distributions were averaged to derive the best distribution of crop and animal incomes in Turkey which can be obtained from the available data. The results are shown in column (3) of Table 6.[13]

TABLE 6

UPPER AND LOWER LIMIT DISTRIBUTION OF NET CROP AND ANIMAL
INCOMES AND THE AVERAGE OF THESE TWO DISTRIBUTIONS

Percent of all farm families	Lower limit distribution: assuming that animal incomes are distributed as they are in the Village Study[a]	Upper limit distribution: assuming that animal incomes are the same per decare of land operated for large and small farmers[b]	Average of upper and lower limit distributions in cols. (1) and (2)[c]
	(1)	(2)	(3)
Lowest 10%	1.06	0.95	1.00
2nd lowest 10%	1.51	1.37	1.44
3rd lowest 10%	2.31	2.09	2.20
4th lowest 10%	3.25	2.96	3.11
5th lowest 10%	4.35	3.96	4.15
6th lowest 10%	5.67	5.19	5.43
7th lowest 10%	7.19	6.61	6.90
8th lowest 10%	9.65	8.94	9.30
9th lowest 10%	14.12	13.28	13.70
Highest 10%	50.89 \newline 100%[d]	54.65 \newline 100%	52.77 \newline 100%[d]

a. This is the same distribution as the one in Table 5. For explanations see
    the notes to Table 5.

b. The method used to derive this distribution is identical to that used to
    derive the distribution in column (1), except that in this case the dis-
    tribution is calculated on the assumption that the gross incomes per de-
    care from animals of both large and small farms within provinces corres-
    pond to the average level in the nation of TL. 15, and that their net ani-
    mal incomes are 20% lower. (For the figure of TL. 15, see note c of
    Table 4; the cost ratio of 20% is the average ratio in the Village Study
    derived from Appendix A, Table 3.) These changes were made in Table 4,
    (lines 4, 5, 6, but lines 1, 2, 3, were left unchanged), and then the dif-
    ference in the net crop and animal incomes per decare for large and small
    farmers within provinces (line 7) was recalculated. The new difference
    was then used to modify the distribution of incomes between provinces in
    Table 1 of this chapter.

c. Derived by averaging the distributions in columns (1) and (2).

d. Percentages do not add up to 100 due to rounding.

CHAPTER IX

THREE FINAL DISTRIBUTIONS OF INCOME FROM
AGRICULTURAL AND NON-AGRICULTURAL SOURCES
EARNED BY THE TURKISH FARM POPULATION

The work described in Chapter VIII produced an
estimate of the proportions of the net crop and
animal income earned by each tenth of farm operators. But the total income to which this
distribution refers has not yet been calculated,
and without this figure the average amounts of
crop and animal income earned by the farm operators in each tenth of the distribution cannot be
determined. The total and average incomes are
calculated in Part I of this chapter.

I. Net Income of Farm Operators from Their Operations

The net crop and animal income whose distribution was estimated in the previous chapter
is the income that farm operators derive from operating their own farms. To determine the total
of this income one must deduct from the national
income originating in agriculture paid agricultural wages and paid land rent,[1] since these incomes, though earned in the agricultural sector,
are part of the costs of farm operations.

A. Paid Wages

Wages paid to agricultural labor were calculated in Chapter II. The amount derived was
TL. 334 million.[2]

B. Paid Rent

The data most directly pertinent for estimating total rent payments pertain to 1963.
The agricultural census of 1950 contains statis-

tics on the number of farm families who rent
land, but does not show the amount of land that
is rented, as does the 1963 census. Since a
given number of families could rent more or less
land than in proportion to their numbers, the
1963 data are considerably more useful. This is
why these data were used, at least in part, even
though a rent figure is needed that pertains to
the early 1950's.

As a first step in deriving this figure,
the 1963 area rented data were converted into
rent payments by assuming (a) that the proportion of the total crop income earned by tenants
is equal to the proportion of all farm land that
they rent, and (b) that average rent payments are
equal to the average portion of the crop paid in
share arrangements. This gave the proportion of
the total agricultural income that tenants paid
to their landlords in 1963. Since the rent data
are needed for 1951, this proportion was then
applied to the 1951 crop income. According to
these calculations total rent payments in 1951
amounted to TL. 229 million.[3]

A question arises about the usability of
the 1963 data, since tenancy conditions might
have changed between 1951 and 1963, and as a result the proportion of rented land might differ
from the proportion in the early 1950's. The
only evidence that bears on this question are
statistics on the percentage of farm families
who were tenants in 1950 and 1963. These percentages increased somewhat during the period in
question, but if proportion of families who are
tenants is an indication of proportion of farm
land that is rented (according to the data in the
1963 Census of Agriculture this assumption is
valid),[4] the increase would not make any significant difference for the estimate of total rent
payments.[5]

C. Conclusion

Subtracting the figures derived above

(TL. 334 million paid wages and TL. 229 million
paid rent) from the sum of factor incomes originating in agriculture of TL. 4,761 million,[6] a
figure of TL. 4,198 million is derived. This is
the income that farmers earn from their operations, and Table 1 (see page 144) shows the total
income and average income earned by each tenth of
farm operators.

II.   Distributions of Total Income Earned
by Farm Operators and by the
Agricultural Population

The distribution of income from farm operations derived in the first part of this chapter is not a distribution of all incomes that
farm operators earn, nor even of all incomes from
agricultural sources. The income that farm operators derive from farm operations is net of all
costs of production, including paid factor costs.
However, some factor costs paid out by some farmers are incomes to other farmers who own these
factors of production. For example, land rent
was deducted as a cost in deriving the previous
distribution, but to the extent to which this
land is rented from farm rather than urban families, it is also an income to other farm families. The same is also true of paid interest
and paid wages. Moreover farmers also earn incomes from non-agricultural sources. Therefore
total earnings of farm operators are larger than
those counted so far. In addition, there are
landless farm workers who operate no farms but
are part of the agricultural population. These
workers (both their numbers and earnings) were
not included in the previous estimates.

In the remainder of this chapter the attempt will be made to derive the distribution of
income from all sources earned by the Turkish
farm population. This involves adding to the
distribution of income from farm operations the
supplementary incomes from both agricultural and

TABLE 1

AVERAGE NET INCOME AND PERCENT OF TOTAL NET INCOME
DERIVED FROM FARM OPERATIONS BY EACH
TENTH OF FARM FAMILIES

Percent of all farm families by income size[a]	Percent of total net income derived from farm operations[b]	Average net income per farm family (TL.)[c]
(1)	(2)	(3)
Lowest 10%	1.00	167
2nd lowest 10%	1.44	239
3rd lowest 10%	2.20	366
4th lowest 10%	3.11	516
5th lowest 10%	4.15	690
6th lowest 10%	5.43	902
7th lowest 10%	6.90	1145
8th lowest 10%	9.30	1544
9th lowest 10%	13.70	2275
Highest 10%	52.77	8764
	100.00[d]	

Mean income = TL. 1,778

Median income = TL. 843

---

a. The total number of families is 2,527,800.

b. Data from Table 6, Chapter VIII, on p.140.

c. Computed from Table 6 in Chapter VIII by applying the percentage incomes in that table (which are reproduced again in column 2 above) to the total net income of farm operators of TL. 4,198 million, and by dividing the total income thus derived for each income bracket by the number of families in these brackets. The total income of TL. 4,198 million is equal to the estimated sum of factor incomes earned in agriculture, less estimated paid wages and paid rent.

d. Percentages do not add up to 100 due to rounding.

non-agricultural sources earned by farm operators
and landless farm workers. The additional estimates required to obtain this distribution are
derived in five steps: A. Supplementary rental
incomes earned by farm operators. B. Supplementary incomes earned mostly by small farmers.
C. Supplementary incomes earned mostly by well-
to-do farmers. D. Imputed non-agricultural incomes of small and well-to-do farmers. E. Wages
and imputed non-farm incomes of landless farm
workers. In the end, all of these estimates are
combined to derive the final distribution.

A.   Supplementary Rental Incomes Earned by Farm Operators

Among the paid factor costs which are incomes to farm families, only rent seems to be
earned by farm operators in all income ranges.
It may seem surprising that small farmers, too,
rent out land, but such arrangements do not seem
to be unusual. For example, Paul Stirling observed that small farmers rent out land if they
are unable to work it themselves either because
they are old, sick, or lack draft animals, or
while they go to work in town,[7] and Wilhelm von
Flügge reported that he heard of many cases where
poor persons act as landlords.[8] The 1963 Census
of Agriculture, too, shows that small farmers
rent out land, as do the farmers in all land
brackets.[9] But in addition the 1963 census data
indicate another aspect of rental relations in
Turkey, namely that most of the land rented by
farmers is rented from persons who themselves
operate farms.[10] This result is rather surprising since the character of the absentee landlord
is frequently mentioned as typical for the whole
Middle East.[11] Since questions have been raised
about the quality of the 1963 census,[12] there is
the very small possibility that this result stems
from the census' shortcomings. Unfortunately
there are no other statistics bearing on rent
earned with which these data could be compared.

(The rent comparison made earlier referred to rent paid but not earned.) Further, it is not entirely clear precisely how the census tables should be interpreted (see note 10 to chapter IX), and since the census appeared as this book was being revised for publication, I did not have the opportunity to discuss these specific results with the Turkish statisticians in charge of planning and compiling these data. For this reason the estimate of rent earned in this section should be treated as tentative.[13] The data are used nevertheless because (1) no other basis exists for approximating the amount of rent earned by farmers, (2) because it is unlikely that the census figures would not at least vaguely resemble the actual situation, and thus approximate the facts better than mere hearsay generalizations, and (3) because including this type of income, even if the estimate is tentative, appeared to me preferable to omitting it entirely.[14]

The estimate was made as follows: The pertinent information in the census is the area of land that farmers rent out, tabulated by land brackets. These data were then converted into rent earnings in two steps. First, the total lira value of rent earned was estimated by means of the same assumptions as those used earlier to derive the total value of rent paid.[15] The result showed that total rent earned was TL. 169 million in 1951.[16] This total was then distributed among farm operators in the same proportion as the distribution of land rented out by farm operators.[17]

As can be seen in Table 2, (see page 148) the resulting distribution of rent earned is relatively equal--the two lowest decile groups together earned 30 percent of all rent, and the highest 23 percent--and, although the total rent earnings are small (less than 4 percent of the net incomes from farm operations--see note c to Table 2), rent earned has a very equalizing effect, especially on the lowest land brackets.

TABLE 2

DISTRIBUTIONS OF INCOME EARNED BY EACH TENTH OF FARM
OPERATORS FROM LAND RENT ALONE, AND FROM NET FARM
OPERATIONS AND LAND RENT COMBINED

Percent of all farm families by income size[a]	Percent of total income from land rent[b]	Percent of total income from farm operations and land rent[c]
(1)	(2)	(3)
Lowest 10%	17.3	1.6
2nd lowest 10%	13.2	1.9
3rd lowest 10%	8.8	2.4
4th lowest 10%	6.1	3.2
5th lowest 10%	5.3	4.2
6th lowest 10%	6.3	5.5
7th lowest 10%	7.4	6.9
8th lowest 10%	5.4	9.2
9th lowest 10%	7.1	13.5
Highest 10%	23.0	51.7
	100.0	100.0

a. The total number of families is 2,527,800.

b. This is the distribution of land rented out by each
    tenth of the families of farm operators, calculated
    from 1963 Census of Agriculture, pp. 6-7. It is
    assumed that the distribution of rent earned is pro-
    portional to the distribution of land rented out.
        Total rent earnings are estimated to be TL. 169 mil-
    lion. This amount was calculated from the estimated
    total value of rent paid of TL. 229 million (see
    pp. 141-42 above.)   Since the proportion of all farm

land rented from other farmers is taken to be 73%,
the amount of rent earned was taken to be 73% of the
value of rent paid.

c. Derived by adding to the distribution of income from
net farm operations in Table 1 of this chapter, 3.87%
of the income from land rent in column (2) above, and
then expressing the result as a percent of the combined income from net farm operations and land rent.
3.87% is the result of expressing TL. 169 million
(the total of rent earnings) as a percent of TL. 169
million plus TL. 4,198 million (the latter is the net
income from farm operations in Table 1 of this chapter).

B. Supplementary Incomes of Small Farmers

Aside from earning rent, small farmers supplement their revenues from farming in a variety of ways. For one, many farmers do agricultural work for more prosperous farmers during the slack season. To find such work a sizeable number migrate temporarily to other regions where the peak of seasonal activity comes earlier or later than in their own villages and where work can be found when there is none at home. In addition, some families with low incomes send one or more of their members to towns or mining areas for a temporary period to earn wages outside of agriculture, and to bring back their savings. There are also opportunities for earning supplementary incomes in the village which do not involve temporary migration. There are a certain number of businesses located in or near villages where farmers can find local employment, and some local shops and crafts are operated by farmers. But the most important source of locally earned non-farm income is household industry. Farmers sell home-processed forest products such as charcoal, or handicraft products such as hand-woven rugs or textiles, baskets, pottery, etc.

For the purpose of estimating the size of the supplementary incomes that farmers earn from these activities, they are divided into (1) wages earned during temporary migration and (2) all locally earned incomes. This division is made necessary by the method of estimation. How these incomes were distributed is considered in (3) once the over-all amount of these incomes has been estimated.

(1) Wages earned during temporary migration. The amount of agricultural wages earned by farm operators had been derived in Part I.[18] Nearly half a million farmers were found to migrate to other villages to do seasonal agricultural work for an average period of about six weeks a year, and their total earnings were es-

timated at TL. 97 million in 1951. The number
of farmers who look for temporary work in towns
and mining areas is much smaller, only about
100,000,[19] but they stay away for a considerably
longer period, a year and a half on the average.[20]
The additional incomes from this type of migratory work have not yet been estimated, since it
does not originate in agriculture.

To find the size of the supplementary
income farmers derive from temporary non-farm
work, the total number of days they spent away
from their villages was taken as a point of departure.[21] From this had to be deducted travel
time and time needed to find work--arbitrarily
assumed to be ten days per worker--and Sundays
and holidays, a total in all of sixty-five days
a year. The remaining time was taken to represent the number of days actually worked.

Since most of the migratory workers do
unskilled work, these farmers should typically
have earned per day the wage rate paid for this
type of work. A very good source of such wage is
Etibank, the government agency that operates the
nation's mines. Etibank employs largely unskilled workers; in fact, for most part it employs peasants living in the neighborhood of the
mines, so that its wages should be representative of those earned by such workers. The total
number of days these workers actually worked
while away from home, times the daily wage of
Etibank,[22] gives the total city and mining wages
earned by farmers of TL. 119 million.[23]

But only that portion of earnings that
the villagers can save and either send home, or
bring with them when they return to their farms,
represents additions to farm income. The other
part should be treated as extra expenses, since
life in the cities involves costs beyond those
incurred on the farm. The extra expenses include lodging, carfare, the difference between
the cost of food in town relative to its value
on the farm, etc. Data on these expenses are not
available. They are arbitrarily assumed to be

TL. 1 per day per worker, or about one third of
daily earnings, an amount likely to be on the
low side. When these expenses were deducted,
the portion of city wages saved, which should be
counted as a supplement to farm income, was found
to be TL. 77 million.

(2) Locally earned income

(a) Number of farm families who earn these incomes

To estimate the locally earned incomes,
one must first determine how many families are
engaged in each of the activities from which this
income is derived. This is done separately for
1. the number of farm families whose members
work in village businesses as paid employees,
2. those who run local shops, and 3. those engaged in household industries.

1. Relatively few villagers seem to be
employed in local businesses on a paid basis.
According to the 1949 village census, the great
majority of village businesses comprise less
than two workers (including the business operators),[24] suggesting that most are very small family affairs. Only brick kilns, sand and stone
quarries, and oil pressing shops employ more than
two workers (besides the operators), and for lack
of any further information on these businesses
it is assumed that they employ only paid workers
and that the workers are members of farm families.

2. Of the total number of businesses
located in villages, only a small portion seem
to be run by farmers. To determine their number,
it is assumed that most rural non-farm families
operate village businesses, but that no family
runs more than one business. Since there are
more rural businesses than non-farm families,
the excess of the number of businesses over the
number of these families is taken to be village
businesses run by farmers.[25]

3. The 1949 village census lists the total number of farm families who do non-agricultural work in addition to farming.[26] To obtain those who are only engaged in household industry, one must deduct the families who work locally for paid wages and those who operate village shops, estimated in 1. and 2. above,[27] and also the households of village officials, whose work in carrying out their official duties also counts as non-farm activity.[28]

The results show that, of somewhat more than 300,000 farm families who earned incomes from local non-farm activities in 1949, nearly 200,000 were in household industry,[29] 12,000 operated village shops, 20,000 had one of their members employed in local business, and there were 70,000 families of village officials. The last group is likely to belong to the more prosperous village households (see page 155 below) whose non-farm incomes are estimated separately in a later section. The same should also be true of some of the shopkeepers, but probably only of a minority due to the small average size of their operations. The proportion of shops run by large farmers was arbitrarily taken to be 10 percent of all rural shops.

(b) The size of locally earned incomes

The figure of TL. 560 in the national income data[30] as the average income per person earned from domestic and village crafts seems considerably too large for household industry, but too small for the income derived from village shops. Half of this amount for the former group, and double the amount for the latter appears more reasonable. For those employed in local businesses the figure was left unchanged. On the basis of these data the total income from the household industry was estimated to be TL. 58 million, the income from village shops at TL. 13 million, and earnings from local employment as TL. 12 million,[31] or a total of TL. 82 million.

Although the separate estimates of the
supplementary incomes that small farmers earn
from each type of non-farm village activity are
necessarily very rough, it was possible to check
the reasonableness of the total of these incomes.
The Turkish national income data include estimates
of the value added in villages by manufacturing
products for sale (rather than for home consumption) and by commercial activities carried on in
villages.[32]   In 1951 these two sources of income
amounted to TL. 165 million, and although this
figure excludes the value added by services, which
is not estimated for villages, this omission
should be of slight consequence because the value
of services is likely to be very small.

The estimate of TL. 82 million made in
this section of the incomes that farmers earn
from non-farm activities in villages amounts to
half of the total (of TL. 165 million) in the
national income data. This seems reasonable for
the following reason: Nearly one fourth of all
rural families who engage in any kind of non-farm
activity are not engaged in agriculture at all.[33]
By earning the other half of the income from manufacturing and commercial activities in villages,
their earnings per family from these sources are
roughly double those of farm families. With no
farm work on the side, such families should be
able to pursue their non-farm work on a full-time
basis, and therefore on the average earn more income from these sources than farm families, for
most of whom non-farm work is only a side activity.

Adding together the supplementary income
of small farmers estimated in this section, one
derives a figure of TL. 256 million. It comprises,
aside from the TL. 82 million obtained from manufacturing and commercial activities, TL. 97 million earned in agricultural wages and TL. 77 million of extra income earned by those who temporarily migrate to towns or mining areas.

(3)   <u>The distribution of supplementary incomes earned by small farmers</u>.   Having derived a figure for the supplementary income of small farmers, the next step is to consider how this income is distributed.   The only source of data on this subject is the Village Study.   These data are presented in Table 3   (see page 156) which shows the average amount earned by the families in each land bracket from (a) wages, (b) household industry, and (c) shopkeeping, horseshoeing, and wholesaling.

The differences in the average amounts earned by the farmers in each land bracket in Table 3 are differences that can be expected on reasonable grounds for lines (b) and (c).   It makes sense that only relatively small farmers, not those in the highest land bracket, derive incomes from household industry (line B), or that, on a per farm basis, the large farmers would get the most income from commercial activities (line C).   But a question arises about the figures in line (A), since large farmers are shown to earn nearly as much in wages as the farmers in the lowest land bracket, and considerably more than those in the intermediate brackets.   This is puzzling because farmers with over 500 decares are quite well off, at least relatively speaking, and one does not expect them to seek extra incomes from menial sources.   However, the wages in the Village Study also include "salaries" of village heads and religious leaders.   Village heads are frequently chosen from among large farmers because their greater income gives them more prestige in the village,[34] and many religious leaders should also belong to the more prosperous households.   Since it seems that the "wages" earned by large farmers are really "salaries," and do not belong to the class of incomes earned by small farmers, it follows that, in estimating the distribution of these incomes for small farmers alone, all revenues of the highest land bracket in Table 3 should be disregarded.

TABLE 3

SUPPLEMENTARY INCOMES EARNED BY THE FARMERS IN THE
VILLAGE STUDY AND NET INCOME FROM CROPS AND
ANIMALS EARNED BY THESE FARMERS (In TL.)

	Farms by land-size brackets (in decares)			
Average income per farm[a] from:	10-79	80-159	160-499	500 and over
	(1)	(2)	(3)	(4)
A. Paid wages[b]	110	76	14	91
B. Household industry	7	13	7	–
C. Shopkeeping, horse-shoeing, and whole-saling[c]	47	31	37	110
D. Total, lines A to C	164	120	58	201
E. Net income from crops, animals and rent[d]	954	1561	3423	12047

Source: From Village Study, Table 35, and computed
from ibid., Table 2.

a. The average income per farm in lines A to D are average
incomes per farm in each land bracket of all farmers
in that land bracket, whether they derive incomes from
this source or not.

b. These earnings include: wages earned in cash or kind
when working for other farmers for pay, remunerations
earned by village heads and religious leaders, and
money brought back by members of families who went to
work in a distant town or city.

c. In the Village Study the second of the incomes in line
3 is referred to as "animal repair." It is assumed
that this refers to horse-shoeing since veterinarians
cannot be expected to live in villages.

d. See Appendix A, Table 1.

To derive the distribution of the supplementary incomes of TL. 256 of small farmers,
it is assumed that the distribution of such earnings in the Village Study is representative of
the country as a whole, but only among the three
lowest land brackets. Table 3 shows that these
incomes per farm decline as farm size increases
up to a point inside the third lowest land bracket.
The decline, as has been suggested, can be explained by the fact that the smaller the income
of the farmer, the more need there is for sub-
sidiary menial activity. Since the income earned
by those in the highest income group seems to be
income of an entirely different kind, it will be
considered below. So far as the former type of
income is concerned, it is earned only by the
two lowest land brackets and the smaller farmers
in the third land bracket. If one assumes that
the difference between the supplementary income
per farm of the two lowest land brackets is an
indication of the extent to which farmers with
less land, and therefore lower incomes, derive
higher additional earnings from these sources
than those with greater incomes, one can determine the distribution of these additional incomes
among small farmers. By using simple proportions,
one obtains the rate at which these incomes decline as one moves from the average income from
farm operations and rent in the lowest land bracket to that of the second lowest,[35] and by extrap-
olating this rate beyond the two land brackets
from which it is derived, one arrives at zero
supplementary incomes when earnings from farm
operations and rent reach TL. 3,216, which corresponds to a land size of roughly 250 decares
in the Village Study.[36]

This distribution of supplementary incomes of small farmers in the Village Study was
then generalized to all small farmers in Turkey
by assuming that these incomes are earned by all
farmers with incomes lower than the average income
of TL. 3,216 of a farm with 250 decares in the
Village Study, and that among these farmers the

supplementary incomes are distributed in the
same proportion as in the distribution derived
from the Village Study.[37] The results of these
estimates are presented in Table 4 (see page 159).
To show more vividly how these supplementary incomes add to those derived from other sources,
the data in Table 4 are presented for each tenth
of farm operators as average incomes per farm,
and the table includes not only the supplementary earnings of small farmers, but all other incomes as well, and for all income groups. Beginning with the columns on the left of the table,
up to column 8, the data show the average earnings per farm from sources estimated at the beginning of this chapter: incomes derived by farm
operators from their own farms (column 2), rent
earned by farmers from renting land to other
farmers (column 3), the total from these two
sources (column 4). The next columns show also
as average incomes per farm the supplementary
incomes of small farm operators estimated in this
section: seasonal agricultural wages (column 5),
temporary wages earned in towns and mining areas
(column 6), locally earned non-farm incomes--
derived from household industry, operating of
village shops, local employment--(column 7), the
total of these three types of supplementary incomes (column 8). To facilitate a comparison of
all incomes earned by farm operators, incomes
whose size and distribution will only be derived
later in this chapter are also included in this
table (columns 9 to 13).

It will be noticed that, according to the
results presented in Table 4, the supplementary
incomes of small farmers are earned by 90 percent
of all farm operators. It may seem puzzling that
so large a portion of the families in the distribution should be typed as "small farmers." This,
of course, is a matter of terminology and,
although this terminology appears reasonable to
the author in light of the low average income
level of even the second highest tenth of the
families in this distribution, this terminology

TABLE 4

AVERAGE INCOME PER FARM EARNED BY EACH TENTH OF FARM OPERATORS FROM AGRICULTURAL SOURCES AND NON-AGRICULTURAL SOURCES, INCLUDING IMPUTED INCOMES, AND THE PERCENT DISTRIBUTION OF THE TOTAL INCOME FROM ALL SOURCES

Average income per farm in TL.

Percent of all farm families by income size[a] (1)	Incomes from farm operations and land rent			Supplementary incomes earned by small farmers					Total non-imputed incomes (cols. 4+8+9) (10)	Imputed incomes[i] (11)	Total incomes from all sources (cols. 10+11) (12)	Percent of total income from all sources in col. 12 (13)
	Farm operations[b] (2)	Land rent[c] (3)	Total (4)	Agricultural wages[dg] (5)	City and mining wages[eg] (6)	Incomes earned in villages[fg] (7)	Total (8)	Other supplementary incomes[h] (9)				
Lowest 10%	167	112	278	55	43	46	144	-	423	47	470	2.46
2nd lowest 10%	239	85	324	54	43	45	142	-	466	48	514	2.70
3rd lowest 10%	366	57	423	52	41	44	137	-	560	50	610	3.20
4th lowest 10%	516	40	556	50	39	42	131	-	686	53	739	3.88
5th lowest 10%	690	35	725	46	37	40	122	-	848	56	904	4.74
6th lowest 10%	902	42	943	42	34	36	112	-	1055	61	1116	5.85
7th lowest 10%	1145	50	1195	38	30	31	99	-	1294	66	1360	7.14
8th lowest 10%	1544	37	1581	30	24	26	80	-	1661	74	1735	9.10
9th lowest 10%	2275	50	2325	17	13	14	44	-	2368	89	2458	12.89
Highest 10%	8764	161	8926	-	-	-	-	-	8926	231	9157	48.03 / 100%
Total income of all families from each source (in millions of TL.)	4198	169	4367	97	77	82	256	-	4623	196	4819	

159

a. The total number of families is 2,527,800.

b. From Table 1 in this chapter.

c. Calculated from Table 2 in this chapter. For details, see Section II A above.

d. "Agricultural wages" refer to wages earned by farm operators who do seasonal agricultural work for other farmers. (See Section II B(1) above.)

e. "City and mining wages" refer to the extra income earned by farmers who temporarily work in cities and mining areas. (See Section II B(1) above.)

f. "Incomes earned in villages" are non-agricultural incomes that farmers earn in or near their own villages and include incomes derived from household industry, operating of village shops, and local employment. (See Section II B(2) above.)

g. The distribution of these incomes was estimated as follows: The total supplementary incomes in col. (8) were taken to decline by TL. 0.0725 as incomes from farm operations and rent increased by TL. 1 between income levels of TL. 954 and TL. 3,216, where TL. 954 is the average income from these sources earned by the lowest land bracket in the Village Study, and TL. 3,216 is the level at which supplementary incomes attributable to small farmers in the Village Study were found to be zero. (For the derivation of this rate see p.287 note 36 below.) For incomes below TL. 954 the supplementary incomes were extrapolated at the same rate, and no supplementary incomes were attributed to farmers with incomes above TL. 3,216. In the end the total supplementary incomes for each tenth of farm operators estimated in this manner were adjusted, proportionately for all income groups, to assure that their sum be equal to the total of these incomes of TL. 256 million (see p.154 above) and then divided by the number of farm families corresponding to each tenth of the distribution.

The incomes in cols. 5, 6, and 7 were derived on the assumption that they are distributed as the total of these incomes is distributed in col. (8).

160

h. This column should have an entry for the highest 10%
    of farm families. For reasons indicated in the text,
    these could not be calculated. (See Section II D of
    this chapter.)

i. These incomes consist of imputed incomes derived from
    processing goods on farms for home consumption, and
    of imputed rent on village dwellings. (See Section II
    D of this chapter.)

was not intentional. Rather, in the course of estimating the upper income limit at which farmers would still earn the types of supplementary income that one associates with small farmers, this result was suggested by the data. Thus it will be recalled that the income level in the Village Study at which the supplementary incomes ascribed to small farmers cease to be earned corresponds to the average income of TL. 3,216 of a farm with 250 decares, and in the distribution by tenth of all farm operators in Table 4 it turned out that this level of income falls almost on the dividing line between the incomes from farm operations and rent of the highest and second-highest tenth of all farm families.[38]

C. Supplementary Incomes Earned Mostly by Well-To-Do Farmers

Unfortunately no allowance could be made in the estimates for the supplementary incomes of farm operators in the highest tenth of the distribution. Although the Village Study contains information on such incomes for the farmers in the highest land bracket, not all of these are likely to be typical for the country as a whole; in addition they do not seem to be sufficiently inclusive.

In the Village Study these incomes derive from shopkeeping and wholesaling (horseshoeing, which is grouped with these commercial types of incomes is probably done mostly by smaller farmers), and some from salaries of village officials. It is the income from wholesaling that sould be atypical. The main commercial crop in Central Anatolia is wheat, and during the year of the Village Study survey all wheat was purchased by the Turkish Soil Products Office, a government agency, at support prices. Therefore little opportunity for private wholesaling existed in the area included in the Village Study.

In addition, the Village Study does not mention one source of income that wealthy farmers earn, namely interest on borrowed funds. Apparently no questions were asked during the Village Study survey about money lending activities and the income derived from it, and no other data are available on privately earned interest in agriculture. While the opportunity for private individuals to lend money to peasants should have declined after 1950, as a result of the liberal amount of credit extended by the Agricultural Bank of Turkey both to small and well-to-do farmers, it is unlikely that private money lending has disappeared. It is the general impression that a good deal of it still exists.

Since no other data on these types of incomes earned by large farmers exist, the supplementary incomes of this group cannot be estimated. In Table 4 this is indicated by the fact that no entry is made in column 8 for the highest tenth of income earners.

D. Imputed Non-Agricultural Income of Small and Well-To-Do Farmers

The incomes from non-agricultural sources considered so far have included only paid incomes. The national income accounts also include imputed incomes. One source of such income derives from processing of farm products for home consumption.[39] Its value was estimated at TL. 94 million in 1951,[40] and presumably includes the estimated imputed income from all non-agricultural production for home consumption done on farms. On a per farm-family basis it amounts to TL. 37. These earnings were distributed equally among the farm population in the present estimates. This was done because most of it is derived from processing of food, especially cereals[41] (which probably includes baking of bread), and in non-drought years the value added by this activity is likely to be proportional to family size rather than income. Although the richer farmers should

have larger households, including servants and
fieldhands, this should be offset by the fact
that they use more goods bought in stores.

Another type of imputed income is rent
of farm dwellings of TL. 102 million.[42]   Since
wealthier farmers have more elaborate homes than
poorer ones, it was assumed that this income is
distributed in proportion to the income from all
other sources.   Therefore the addition of imputed
rent does not change the distribution of income
derived so far (for farm operators) but only
raises all incomes proportionally.

Imputed rents are the only imputed income from services included in the national income estimates.   Theoretically there should also
be imputed income from personal services which
villagers do themselves or render to others
without payment, and for which money is paid in
communities that are less self-sufficient than
many of the Turkish villages, and an imputed
value for these services should be added to farm
incomes.   No basis for such an estimate exists,
but the omitted income is probably small.

The distribution of the two types of imputed incomes is shown in Table 4 (column 11),
which shows the average amount of these incomes
earned by each tenth of farm operators.

E.   Final Distribution for Farm Operators

Table 4 includes all incomes earned by
farm operators for which estimates could be made
and shows, for all income brackets except the
highest, the relative importance of the various
sources of income.   It is seen that the lowest
10 percent of these families derives from farm
operations only about one third of their income;
income from rent constitutes an important addition to their incomes from farming,[43] the supplementary incomes in column (8) add an even
larger amount, and even the imputed incomes are
not negligible relative to the size of incomes
from other sources.

The table shows, too, that as incomes from farming increase, the relative importance of earnings from sources other than farm operations declines. For example, for the second highest tenth of the families, farming provides over 95 percent of all earnings. Unfortunately this comparison cannot be made for the highest group, since the magnitude of their supplementary incomes, aside from earned rent and imputed incomes, could not be estimated. As a result the overall distribution of all incomes earned by farm operators in column (13) is more equal than it should be.

F.   Wages and Imputed Non-Farm Incomes of Landless Farm Workers

The distribution of income in Table 4 excludes the incomes and families of landless farm workers. These could only be added at the end because it is only when the distribution of income of farm operators from all sources is known that the position in this distribution at which the extra families should be incorporated could be determined.

The number of these families and their incomes were estimated in Chapter II. They comprise 310,000 families and their average income was TL. 763 per year, including wages and imputed incomes.[44] In Table 4 this income falls into the earnings range of the fourth lowest 10 percent of farm operators. Therefore the landless workers and their incomes were incorporated into the distribution of income earned by farm operators at this level. After they were added, the distribution was rearranged so that each of the ten income brackets in the distribution would include the incomes earned by one tenth of the increased number of families.

G.   The Final Distribution of Income among the Turkish Farm Population

The final distribution, which includes

the earnings of landless farm workers, is shown
in Table 5 (see page 167). It is the best estimate that could be derived of the distribution
of income, from all sources, earned by families
engaged in agriculture.

According to Table 5 the lowest tenth of
all farmers get only 2.7 percent of all income
earned by farm families, a proportion that is
extremely small. There is little doubt that
these families earn an even smaller portion of
income from operating their own farms, and from
renting out land, but one would have expected
that supplementary incomes from migratory farm
wages and from non-agricultural sources would
have raised the share of the total income for the
poorest farmers more than is shown in Table 5.
This raises the question of the extent of the
possible error that may have been introduced into
the estimates by the method of apportioning the
supplementary incomes among small farmers. It
will be recalled that, for lack of more specific
information, the assumption was made that these
supplementary incomes are distributed as they
are in the Village Study. But since the income
range of the lowest land bracket in the Village
Study corresponds roughly to that of the seven
lowest tenths of all farmers in the nation, the
distribution of these earnings within this range
could not be derived directly, but was extrapolated from the distribution of these earnings in
the Village Study among families whose incomes
correspond to those of the sixth and ninth decile
groups in the nation. It is possible that the
assumption made in this straight-line extrapola-
tion is not correct, i.e., that as incomes from
farm operations and rent decline, supplementary
incomes of small farmers increase, not in constant proportions, as had been assumed, but more
than proportionally. Since this is a distinct
possibility, it is well to estimate the size of
the possible error that may have resulted from
using this assumption. This can be done as follows: The assumption in question does not affect

TABLE 5

DISTRIBUTION OF INCOME, FROM ALL SOURCES, EARNED BY
EACH TENTH OF FAMILIES ENGAGED IN AGRICULTURE

Percent of all families[a]	Percent of total income (in %)[b]	Average income per family (in TL.[b])
Lowest 10%	2.66	475
2nd lowest 10%	3.00	535
3rd lowest 10%	3.66	652
4th lowest 10%	4.22	751
5th lowest 10%	4.56	812
6th lowest 10%	5.61	1,000
7th lowest 10%	7.04	1,254
8th lowest 10%	9.05	1,612
9th lowest 10%	12.91	2,300
Highest 10%	47.29	8,425
	100.00	

a. These families include 2,527,800 farm operators and
   310,000 landless workers, or a total of 2,837,800
   families.

b. The total income, from all sources, earned by all families engaged in agriculture, includes all incomes in
   Table 4 of TL. 4,819 million, plus the wages earned by
   the 310,000 families of landless workers of TL. 237
   million, or a total income of TL. 5,056 million.

the proportion of all income (from supplementary as well as other non-imputed sources) of the seven lowest decile groups combined, which is 30.8 percent in Table 5; on the average per decile group, for the seven lowest groups, this comes to 4.4 percent. Since it is most unlikely that the distribution of supplementary incomes among the poorest 70 percent of farm families had a perfectly equalizing effect, i.e., fully compensated for the inequality of income from farm operations and rent among them, one must conclude that the three or four lowest decile groups are almost certain to earn less than four and a half percent, and the lowest group less than 4 percent. Therefore, if the assumption in apportioning the supplementary incomes of small farmers had been too unequalizing, it is most improbable that the share of all income earned by the poorest tenth of all farm families in the final distribution is understated by more than approximately one percentage point.

It should be noted that these considerations only affect the distribution of income among the seven lowest tenths of the families in the final distribution, but not of their combined share of total income. As a result these questions do not involve the proportions of all income that are earned by the three highest decile groups, and have no bearing on the fact that the income of the highest tenth of the families in Tables 4 and 5 is lower than it should be since the supplementary incomes of this group could not be estimated at all.

III. Summary and Conclusion to Part II

The analysis of income distribution by income size has pointed up some of the significant factors that make for more or less inequality of income among Turkish farmers and farm workers. The estimates began with the distribution of land operation because these date were

the only ones that had any direct bearing on inequality of agricultural incomes by size of income, and the distribution was then modified step
by step to take account of factors other than
size of farm that affect inequality. Although
this method was devised primarily as a means of
deriving the final distribution, since the available data did not enable a more direct approach,
one by-product of this method is that it also
shows what factors make for greater or lesser inequality of income distribution among Turkish
farmers, and the relative strength of these factors. Another by-product, which derives from
the first, is that the breakdown into equalizing
and unequalizing factors helps to point up the
effect on income distribution of some of the
major changes in economic conditions and institutions in the agricultural sector.

The distribution of land operated as
well as the results of the major distributions
derived by this method are presented in Table 6
(see page 170). The table shows that the final
distribution in column (6) is more equal than
that of land operated in column (1), but it is
useful to analyze the relation of the first four
columns alone to begin with. Thus if one com-
pares the distribution of income that farmers
derive from operating their own farms (or from
crop and animal incomes) in column (4) with that
of land operated in column (1) it turns out that
the two distributions are very similar in degree
of inequality (since the share of the total of
both the richer and poorer farmers is somewhat
larger in column (4) than in column (1), the degree of inequality should be about the same).
This similarity is in part caused by the fact
that size of land operation is one of the basic
factors creating inequality of incomes from farm
operation; but other factors play a role too,
some tending to create greater inequality and
some less, and on balance there is a great deal
of cancelling of opposing forces.

TABLE 6

DISTRIBUTION OF LAND OPERATED AND THE PARTIAL AND FINAL ESTIMATES OF THE DISTRIBUTION OF INCOME EARNED BY FARM FAMILIES: A SUMMARY[1]

		Percent of total income derived by each tenth of farm operators from each of the following sources:				
Percent of farm families	Percent of all land operated	Gross crop income	Net crop income	Net crop and animal income (farm operations)	All agricultural and non-agricultural sources	Farm operators and landless workers from all sources
	(1)	(2)	(3)	(4)	(5)	(6)
Lowest tenth	1.8 ⎫	.7	.8	1.0	2.5	2.7
2nd lowest tenth	⎭	1.1	1.2	1.4	2.7	3.0
3rd lowest tenth	2.1	1.8	2.0	2.2	3.2	3.7
4th lowest tenth	3.2	2.6	2.8	3.1	3.9	4.2
5th lowest tenth	4.5	3.3	3.6	4.2	4.7	4.6
6th lowest tenth	5.7	4.4	4.7	5.4	5.9	5.6
7th lowest tenth	7.5	5.9	6.3	6.9	7.1	7.0
8th lowest tenth	10.1	8.0	8.5	9.3	9.1	9.1
9th lowest tenth	15.3	12.3	12.9	13.7	12.9	12.9
Highest tenth	49.8	60.0	57.3	52.8	48.0	47.3
	100	100	100	100	100	100

[1]The distributions summarized in this table have been shown on pp. 83, 104, 117, 140, 159, and 167.

The factor which makes for greater inequality is higher crop incomes per decare of large compared to small farmers. Its unequalizing force is very strong. Disregarding costs for the moment, the distribution of gross crop incomes is considerably more unequal than that of land operated (compare column 2 to column 1). The main reason is that many of the large farms are located in regions suitable for growing very lucrative crops. While there are many very small farms in the Black Sea region, one of Turkey's most fertile areas, a high proportion of the large farms are located in the rich river valleys of the Aegean region and the fertile alluvial Çukurova valley in the Mediterranean, and on balance the good location of the large farms was found to predominate over that of the small.

Even within the same region it was found that large farmers generally grow more lucrative crops than small ones. Large farms are mostly commercial farms and as such avail themselves of the advantages of specialization (and grow as lucrative crops as soil and climate permit) far more than small farms which produce primarily for subsistence. It is true that in regions where crops that yield a higher than average return per decare cannot be grown and marketed in quantity, as in Central Anatolia, small farmers seem to derive a larger gross return per decare, for they grow a larger proportion of crops that yield a relatively high income per decare, such as fruit and vegetables, than large farmers. But this difference is largely illusory, a result of assigning to these crops their market price. Were a big enough market available to make it worthwhile for larger farmers to grow these crops one would expect the relation to be reversed. This is shown more clearly in regions where the more lucrative crops, like cotton, can be grown and marketed. Here large farmers devote a considerably greater proportion of their area to these crops than small farmers do. In spite of the probable over-valuation of home-consumed crops for which no correction could be made, it was found that on balance differences in types of crops grown make for inequality. In the long run, however, this factor should become less important if the small farmer is brought within the orbit of the market system to a larger extent and is thereby enabled to avail himself of some of the advantages of specialization more than he does now.

A final and very important reason why gross crop incomes in column (2) are distributed more unequally than land operated in column (1) is that large farmers are fairly mechanized. Mechanization increases yields because in Turkey the shortage of draft power, coupled with the limited period during which plowing must be completed, prevents the average farmer during the average year from finishing his plowing on time, or plowing the fields as often as he should, with the result that yields are considerably lower than the maximum that could be achieved. By overcoming these handicaps with tractors, about a quarter of all large farmers have been able to increase their crop output and income per decare by a significant proportion.[45]

Tractors, of course, have affected the distribution of crop income in still other ways. They resulted in some displacement of sharecroppers and caused large farmers to buy and rent more land--in some cases from small ones-- and to use land which they had previously rented out to small farmers, thereby increasing inequality. Most important, their introduction gave a strong impetus to the movement of plowing up more and more pasture land, mostly by large or medium size farmers. These effects cannot be seen in the comparison of the distributions in Table 6 since they also resulted in greater inequality in the distribution of land operated which forms the basis of this comparison.

Net crop incomes in column (3) are distributed more equally than gross crop incomes in column (2) because costs account for a larger

proportion of the gross crop incomes of large
than small farmers. Large farmers have higher
operational expenses since they must pay either
for labor or labor-saving equipment; it was also
found that they pay somewhat more rent than small
farmers as they operate a greater proportion of
rented land, partly as a result of the tractor
program. But the large farmers' higher crop costs
go only a small way toward offsetting their
higher gross crop incomes per decare, and on balance the distribution of net crop incomes is still
considerably more unequal than that of land operated.

The main factor that reduces inequality
is animal incomes. Their distribution largely
cancels the unequalizing effect of crop incomes
and causes the combined distribution of crop and
animal incomes in column (4) to be similar in degree of inequality to that of land operated in
column (1). Because the use of common grazing
land gives small farmers greater access to pastures than to crop land, small farmers derive a
considerably larger portion of their incomes
from animals and animal products than large
farmers. Without question this is the most important factor making for greater equality of
agricultural incomes. It should be noted that
the equalizing effect of animal incomes has di-
minished after 1952; as more and more pasture
land was plowed up and the number of livestock
grazing on these shrinking pastures continued
to grow, there is evidence that absolute diminishing returns from the use of the common pasture
land set in. By reducing the income that could
be derived from the common pastures these developments have also reduced the equalizing effect
of animal incomes.[46]

The total income of farm operators from
both agricultural and non-agricultural sources
in column (5) is more equally distributed than
the income of the same families from crops and
animals alone in column (4). A number of fac-

tors contribute to this result. For one, small farmers own land they do not work themselves, for example land inherited in distant villages, and earn rent by letting it out, and there is some evidence that families who operate extremely small farms earn somewhat more land rent than those with large farms.

Secondly, small farmers derive supplementary incomes from sources other than land they operate or own. Many earn agricultural wages by migrating seasonally to agricultural regions where the peak of activity comes earlier or later than at home; others migrate to towns or mining areas and work there for a temporary period. A small number find jobs in or near their village, or operate small shops as a side activity. A large proportion engage in some form of household industry. Since farmers whose income from farm operations alone is inadequate must find other sources of revenue, and since the pressure is greatest on those whose income from farming is least, inclusion of these supplementary types of incomes almost certainly makes for greater equality. But the equalizing effect should be smaller than shown in Table 6 as the non-agricultural incomes of large farmers could not be included in the table for lack of data.

A minor reason why the distribution in column (5) is more equal than that in column (4) is that it comprises imputed non-agricultural incomes. Those derived from home-processing of farm products for family consumption were assumed to be very equally distributed, and although imputed rent on farm dwellings was taken to be distributed as unequally as incomes from all other sources, on balance the addition of imputed incomes had a somewhat equalizing effect.

The final distribution in column (6), which includes not only farm operators, but now also landless farm workers (and the total income of both groups), is only slightly more unequal than the corresponding distribution in column (5)

for farm operators. Although the average income
of landless families was found to be a good deal
lower than the median income of farm operators,
inclusion of these families has only a slightly
equalizing effect because landless peasants do
not comprise a very large proportion of the Turkish farm population.

COST OF CROPS, WORK ANIMALS, AND NON-WORK ANIMALS,
AND NET CROP AND ANIMAL INCOMES
IN THE VILLAGE STUDY

The purpose of this Appendix is to separate crop
costs from animal costs in the Village Study data
and to use the resulting estimates in determining
the net incomes of farms of different sizes.

A summary of the income and costs derived
from crops, animals, rent, etc., in the Village
Study is shown in Table 1 (see page 177). While
the table separates the income from the different
sources, the difficulty in evaluating the net incomes from crops and animals is that there is no
logical separation of crop and animal costs.
Work animals help in producing crops, so that
their costs should be ascribed to crops, while
non-work animals, chiefly sheep and goats, give
rise to animal incomes--milk products, wool,
meat, etc.--and their costs should be ascribed
to these animal incomes and not to crops. The
Village Study data do not divide costs among
crop costs, including expenses for work animals,
on the one hand, and the costs of animal products,
which should only consist of expenses for non-
work animals, on the other. This makes it necessary to estimate the share of animal costs that
should be ascribed to each source of income.

The results of these estimates are presented in Tables 2 and 3 (see pages 180, 182
of this appendix). Table 2 shows incomes and
costs relating to crops alone, including the
costs of work animals; Table 3 gives the costs of
non-work animals.

The cost items that had to be estimated
separately for work and non-work animals in pre-
paring Tables 2 and 3 are items 15 and 16 in
Table 1 (the cost of feed and the cost of buildings) both of which combine the cost of work and
non-work animals; item 6 (wages) which combines
wages paid to agricultural workers as well as
shepherd wages, the latter paid both for the
care of work and non-work animals; and item 12

TABLE 1

TOTAL AGRICULTURAL INCOME AND EXPENDITURE IN THE VILLAGE STUDY
BY LAND SIZE BRACKETS[a] (In TL.)

		Farms by land-size brackets (in decares)			
		10-79	80-159	160-499	500 and over	Average, all farms[h]
		(1)	(2)	(3)	(4)	(5)

GROSS INCOME

1.	Gross income from crops	1,037	2,009	4,754	20,783	1,745
2.	Income from animals and animal products	311	510	986	2,501	422
3.	Income from renting out machinery and equipment[b]	3	11	21	97	7
4.	Income from renting out land[c]	1	2	3	25	2
5.	TOTAL GROSS INCOME	1,352	2,532	5,764	23,406	2,175

COSTS

6.	Cost of hired labor	52	254	490	940	126
7.	Seed bought	24	49	143	550	44
8.	Seed produced on farm	100	210	498	2,146	176
9.	Expenditure for equipment (depreciation, repair, spare parts)	22	45	201	1,775	65
10.	Fuel costs[d]	–	–	132	1,293	29
11.	Rent of machinery	3	25	85	425	19
12.	Taxes	23	32	60	155	29
13.	Interest on debts	29	36	101	509	42
14.	Fertilizer	2	10	15	50	5
15.	Feed	39	52	91	104	46
16.	Depreciation and repair of buildings[e]	47	115	164	490	72
17.	Other[f]	34	61	133	324	49
18.	Total cost except land rent	375	889	2,113	8,761	702
19.	Land rent	23	82	228	2,598	85
20.	Total cost[g]	398	971	2,341	11,359	787
21.	NET INCOME	954	1,561	3,423	12,047	1,388

a. From Village Study, Table 2, unless otherwise indicated.

b. The sale of miscellaneous items refers to sale of seed, cow dung, feed, etc.

c. In the Village Study the income from renting out land was listed as a part of "non-farm incomes." It is here included with farm incomes.

d. This cost was left out in Table 2 in the Village Study, presumably by error. It is shown in Table 21 in that study.

e. This item actually refers to "construction and repair of buildings." The reason that the questionnaire asked about construction rather than depreciation is that the concept of depreciation would not have been easily understood by the farmers who were interviewed. The logic behind this procedure is that if buildings are replaced after a number of years, and if such replacement activity is not bunched, the value of the new buildings constructed would approximately represent the extent to which old buildings wear out every year. This assumes, however, that there is no increase in the number of buildings owned by the farmers in these villages and that the new buildings are not better or larger than the old ones. This item is probably somewhat overstated, especially because there should have been some increase in population, and therefore in the number of buildings needed in the villages.

f. This includes expenditures on the following items: costs of small implements, rent of draft animals, seed cleaning, irrigation, animal shoeing, animal vaccination, cost of saddles and harnesses, transportation of the crop to the market and of equipment and materials to the villages, expenditures on baskets, cord, sacks, etc.
   The cost of renting draft animals was erroneously listed twice in Table 2, once among "other expenditures," and also as a separate expenditure. Here it is, therefore, omitted as a separate expenditure.

g. The Village Study adds one other cost to those shown in Table 1 and analysis shows that this figure depreciates the value of the land. This item is called "depreciation of farm capital" and the rate of depreciation is 7% of the value of farm capital. This enables one to calculate the value of the capital for which this depreciation is figured, and this value is almost identical to the value of land owned in Table 28 of the Village Study. This depreciation item was, of course, omitted from the costs in Table 1.

h. These averages are different from those given in the Village Study. As noted earlier, the Village Study includes relatively more large farms than their representative number in the region, so that the weighted averages in the Village Study give too great a weight to the large farms and too little importance to the small ones. To find more representative weights for each land bracket I calculated the relative importance that farms of the land sizes in the Village Study have in regions I and IX in the "1952 Fall Survey" (shown in 1950 Agricultural Census Results, pp. 124-125). The weights derived were 76.83% for the farms in the lowest land bracket, and 14.43%, 7.21% and 1.51% for the farms in the succeeding land brackets. (E.g., 76.83% of all farms in regions I and IX had 10-79 decares, 14.43% had 80-159 decares, etc.) These weights were used to calculate the weighted average in column 5.

TABLE 2

CROP INCOME AND CROP COSTS (INCLUDING INCOMES AND COSTS OF RELATED ITEMS) IN THE VILLAGE STUDY BY LAND SIZE BRACKETS[a] (In TL.)

		Farms by land-size brackets (in decares)			
	10-79	80-159	160-499	500 and over	Average all farms[e]
	(1)	(2)	(3)	(4)	(5)
GROSS INCOME					
1. Gross income from crops	1,037	2,009	4,754	20,783	1,745
3. Income from renting out machinery and equipment and from sale of miscellaneous items	3	11	21	97	7
4. Income from renting out land	1	2	3	25	2
5a. TOTAL GROSS INCOME	1,041	2,022	4,778	20,905	1,754
COSTS					
6a. Cost of hired labor[b]	42	237	460	869	113
7. Seed bought	24	49	143	550	44
8. Seed produced on farm	100	210	498	2,146	176
9. Expenditure for equipment (depreciation, repair, spare parts)	22	45	201	1,775	65
10. Fuel costs	-	-	132	1,293	29
11. Rent of machinery	3	25	85	425	19
12a. Taxes[c]	14	19	29	93	17
13. Interest on debts	29	36	101	509	42
14. Fertilizer	2	10	15	50	5
15a. Feed	24	23	37	25	25
16a. Depreciation and repair of buildings	29	52	67	116	36
17. Other[d]	34	61	133	324	49
18a. TOTAL COST except land rent	323	767	1,901	8,175	620
19. Land rent	23	82	228	2,598	85
20a. TOTAL COST, including land rent	346	849	2,129	10,773	705

a. The item numbers in this table correspond to those in Tables 1 and 3. An "a" following an item number means that only that part of the total lira value of this item in Table 1 which was allocated to crops is included here. In Table 3 below the animal portion of the corresponding items are designated by the same item numbers but followed by a "b".

b. The expenditures listed here are the sum of wages paid to agricultural workers plus the shepherd wages paid for work animals.

c. Of the several types of taxes listed in the Village Study, only land and village taxes were assigned to crops and are included here. (See also note (b) to Table 3 below.)

d. The costs of animal shoeing, animal vaccination, and of saddles and harnesses are included above as costs of crops, as these expenditures would largely be for draft animals.

e. See note (h) to Table 1 above.

TABLE 3

INCOME AND COSTS OF NON-WORK ANIMALS IN THE VILLAGE STUDY
BY LAND-SIZE BRACKETS
(In TL.)[a]

		Farms by land-size brackets (in decares)				
		10-79 (1)	80-159 (2)	160-499 (3)	500 and over (4)	Average all farms[c] (5)
2.	Gross income from animals and animal products	311	510	986	2,501	422
	Costs					
15b.	feed	15.3	28.7	53.8	79.4	20.98
16b.	buildings	18.5	63.5	96.9	374.2	36.05
12b.	taxes[b]	8.6	13.0	30.9	60.5	11.64
6b.	paid shepherd wages	10.3	16.5	29.7	71.0	13.52
20b.	TOTAL COST	52.7	121.7	211.3	585.1	82.19
21b.	Net Income	258.3	388.3	774.7	1,915.9	339.81

a. See note (a) to Table 2 above.

b. Of the several types of taxes listed in the Village Study, animal taxes
were assigned to non-work animals, as they are not levied on work animals;
building taxes were also assigned to non-work animals, since the latter
were found to use the larger part of the buildings (and the error in apportioning this small item among both work and non-work animals is minute).
These two types of taxes are included above.

c. See note (h) to Table 1 above.

(taxes) which are levied on land, buildings, animals, plus a "village tax." How these estimates were made is explained in what follows.

A. The Share of Feed Costs to be Ascribed to Work and Non-Work Animals

To separate the cost of feed that should be assigned to work and non-work animals, all livestock in the Village Study was converted into feed equivalents in order to determine the ratio of work to non-work animals, not in terms of their relative number, but in terms of the relative amount of feed that these two types of animals consume. Once this ratio was calculated, separately for each land bracket, the actual feed expenditures in the Village Study could be divided among work and non-work animals according to these ratios.

The basis for this estimate consists of data given in "A Survey of Grazing and Cattle Production in Erzurum Province."[1] This study expresses all animals in feed units, where one feed unit is equal to the amount of hay and straw consumed by a cow during the winter feeding season, and straw is taken to be worth one half of the feed value of hay.[2] As a first step in determining the proportion of the total feed consumed by these two types of animals, the work and non-work animals owned by the farmers in the Village Study were therefore converted into winterfeed equivalents.

But work animals are also fed during the summer. On the basis of the same survey one could estimate that summer feeding for work animals would roughly triple the total number of feed units for these animals.[3] To include the summer feed, the winter-feed units derived for work animals in step (1) were therefore tripled. As a result of these computations (done separately for each land bracket) all work and non-work animals owned by the farmers in the Village Study were thus expressed in the equivalent a-

mount of feed that each of these two types of
animals consumes both during the winter and summer. It is from these data that the proportion
of total feed consumption of work and non-work
animals in each land bracket was computed.[4]

B. The Share of the Cost of Buildings to be Ascribed to Work and Non-Work Animals

To make this estimate it is assumed that
buildings are used exclusively for animals. This
is not entirely accurate as tractors, too, receive shelter.[5] The error, however, should be
very small. Only the farmers in the highest land
bracket have enough tractors to significantly affect the result,[6] but they also own over 100
sheep and goats, and more than a dozen larger animals.[7] Therefore the shelter for machinery
would only constitute a small part of the shelter
provided for animals and machinery combined, even
for this land bracket. To separate the cost of
buildings for work and non-work animals it was
then assumed that work animals, on the average,
get as much more shelter as they get more feed.
It is true that it is only the share of feed consumed by each animal during the winter, when all
animals are given feed, that would provide some
measure of animal's weight and therefore of the
space it occupies in the shelter. But work animals are far more precious and important to
farmers than non-work animals, and are better
cared for. It therefore seemed more logical to
assume that the relative amount of shelter work
animals receive is greater than in proportion to
their weight, and that it can better be measured
by their share of the total summer plus winter
feed they receive, rather than by their share of
the winter feed alone. Therefore the cost of
buildings of each land bracket in the Village
Study was apportioned among work and non-work animals according to the ratios of the total feed
equivalents calculated for work and non-work animals in the previous section.[8]

C. The Share of Wages to be Ascribed to Shepherds
    for Work and Non-Work Animals and to Agricul-
    tural Workers

        The cost of paid wages was divided among
crops and non-work animals in five steps: 1. A
preliminary estimate of shepherd wages was made
on the basis of observations reported by Paul
Stirling[9] for the village of Central Anatolia
where he lived, by assigning Stirling's shepherd
wage data, which differ for different animals, to
each kind of animal owned by the farmers in the
Village Study.[10] (Where wages were given in
grain they were converted into money according
to 1953 wheat prices indicated in the Village
Study.) 2. These figures were then reduced to
allow for the fact that not all farm families
used the services of paid shepherds. This posed
a problem, however, because the Village Study
provides data on the percentage of families in
each land bracket who hire paid shepherds, but
does not indicate whether these families use paid
shepherds for the total length of time during
which shepherd services are needed, nor whether
they use them for all of their livestock. As a
second preliminary estimate it was nevertheless
assumed that they do, and the data derived in
step 1. were reduced by the proportion given in
the Village Study of the percent of farmers in
each land bracket who use paid shepherds. These
estimates were made separately for work and non-
work animals and for each land bracket. Compared
to the total paid wages shown in the Village Study
the results seemed very large.
        3. To determine whether shepherd wages
could absorb as large a share of total wages as
indicated in the preliminary results, some independent way had to be found to estimate non-shepherd wages in the Village Study. The available
data enabled one to do no more than estimate the
minimum non-shepherd wages paid by the farmers in
the lowest land bracket. The reason is that the
Village Study data on this type of wages only

show (a) the percent of families in each land
bracket that hire labor on a daily, monthly, etc.
basis (and the percent that hire shepherds),[11]
and (b) the wage rates that correspond to each
length of employment[12] (except for shepherd
wages). The data do not indicate how many workers are hired for each period, nor how many are
hired for several successive periods (for example,
monthly labor could be hired for one month or
for several months). Nevertheless, for the lowest land bracket it did not seem unreasonable to
assume that these families would only hire the
minimum number of workers for the mimimum time
indicated in the statistics, i.e., that families
that hire monthly labor hire only one worker for
one month, etc. When the mimimum non-shepherd
wages were estimated in this manner for the lowest land bracket, it turned out that the sum of
these mimimum non-shepherd wages, plus the shepherd wages calculated in step 2. was larger than
the total of paid wages shown for this bracket
in the Village Study. 4. To make the total
agree, shepherd wages had to be reduced by about
one third and this reduction was then also applied
to other land brackets, i.e., for all land brackets both the shepherd wages for work and non-
work animals were reduced by this percentage.
5. All non-shepherd wages were then calculated
as a residual, by deducting the reduced shepherd
wages from the total of paid wages shown in the
Village Study for each of these land brackets.
The wages that are considered animal costs are
those paid to shepherds for non-work animals.
All other wages are taken to be crop costs.[13]

E.   Summary

It is now possible to restate the data
in Table 1 separately for crops and animals.
Table 2 shows the income derived from crops and
the costs assigned to this income. Table 3 gives
the corresponding data for non-work animals.

F.   Cost of Work Animals Stated Separately

Tables 2 and 3, as has been noted, show the separate estimates of incomes and costs that relate to crops and those that relate to non-work animals. However, since for some purposes of analysis in the text it is necessary to separate the costs incurred for work animals from other crop costs, these costs are presented alone in Table 4 (see page 188).

TABLE 4

COST OF WORK ANIMALS IN THE VILLAGE STUDY[a]
(In TL.)

		Farms by land-size brackets (in decares)			
		10-79 (1)	80-159 (2)	160-499 (3)	500 and over (4)	Average all farms[d] (5)
1.	Feed	23.7	23.3	37.2	24.6	24.63
2.	Buildings	28.5	51.5	67.1	115.8	35.93
3.	Animal shoes[b]	11.2	10.0	15.1	17.8	11.41
4.	Saddles and harnesses[b]	12.2	10.9	16.4	19.3	12.42
5.	Vaccination[b]	.8	.7	1.1	1.2	.81
6.	Animal hire[b]	1.3	1.2	1.8	2.1	1.33
7.	Paid shepherd wages	5.9	5.9	8.3	10.3	6.14
8.	TOTAL	83.6	103.5	147.0	191.1	92.67
9.	TOTAL COST except factor costs[c]	76.4	96.4	136.9	178.7	85.2

a. These costs are a part of the "crop costs" included among costs in Table 2.

b. These costs, which are part of item 17 in Table 2, are given separately in the Village Study only as the average for all farms. To estimate their average amount for each land bracket it was assumed that the expenditures on these four items are the same per work animal. These costs were therefor apportioned to the various land brackets according to the relative number of all work animals owned by the farmers in each land bracket in the Village Study.

c. Line 8 minus lines 6 and 7.

d. See note (h) to Table 1 above.

THE RETURN ON INVESTMENTS IN TRACTORS
AND MODERN EQUIPMENT IN THE
MECHANIZATION STUDY

The method of estimating the return on investments in tractors and modern equipment in the Mechanization Study was summarized in the text. The total net return was estimated by figuring the increase in the gross income due to the use of tractors and other modern equipment, and then subtracting from this the cost of this equipment.

The factors that contributed to increase gross income and that were included in these calculations were 1. increase in yields that can be ascribed to tractors and other modern equipment, 2. income earned by mechanized farmers by working land with tractors for others for pay, and 3. savings in the cost of labor and draft animals.

The equipment costs consisted of 1. depreciation of machinery and equipment, 2. cost of repairs and spare parts, and 3. fuel cost.[1]

The resulting net return is then taken as a percentage of the value of the investment in the equipment from which it is derived--minus depreciation--to obtain the rate of return. The details involved in making these calculations are shown below.

I. Increase in Gross Incomes

A. Increase in Gross Incomes Resulting from Increased Yields

To calculate the increase in income due to increased yields derived from mechanized agriculture, the yield data for mechanized and un-

mechanized agriculture given in the Mechanization Study are weighted by the product of the
area planted to each crop and their prices in
1952, and the difference between the total
income with mechanized and unmechanized yields
is then ascertained. More precisely, the method
used for calculating the income from mechanized
agriculture consists of multiplying (1) the area
cultivated with tractors in 1952, separately for
each of the four crops in each of the six regions
for which separate data are given in the Mechanization Study, by (2) their 1952 prices and then
again by (3) the mechanized yields for each crop
and each region. The pre-mechanization income is
calculated by multiplying the yield data by the
same 1952 area and price data, but the yield data
used are those given for unmechanized rather than
mechanized agriculture.

The sources of the data for these calculations as well as the more detailed methods
of estimation are the following:

(1) _Area_. The area devoted to each crop
is shown in Table 59 of the Mechanization Study.
But this table does not indicate what proportion
is cultivated with tractors and what proportion
with animals. Since the costs of tractors that
are to be deducted from the gross incomes of
mechanized agriculture only refer to the area cultivated with tractors, the gross crop income calculated for these farmers in each area should be
limited to the income derived from the mechanized
area alone. Since no data on the mechanized area
of each crop are given in the Mechanization Study,
but data are given on the over-all area in each
region cultivated with tractors and with animals
for all four crops combined, the assumption was
made that in each area the proportion of land
cultivated with tractors and with animals was the
same for each crop. Tables 64 and 65 in the
Mechanization Study give the over-all area cultivated with animals and with tractors respectively, so that the average ratios of the area

cultivated with tractors to the total area cultivated by these farmers could be calculated for
each region. These ratios were then applied to
the area of each crop in each region on the assumption that the degree of mechanization for each
crop was the same. (For example, in the Marmara
region the ratio of the area cultivated with
tractors to the total area planted to the four
crops by sample farmers was 67 percent. It was
then assumed that 67 percent of the area planted
to each of the four crops in the Marmara region
was worked with mechanized equipment.)

(2) Prices

(a) Prices of wheat, barley, and cotton
    For prices of wheat, barley, and cotton,
1952 prices are taken from Agricultural Structure and Production, 1946-1954, p. 2, but were
reduced by 10, 18, and 10 percent respectively.
The 10, 18, and 10 percent reductions were made
because these prices are those received by farmers in provincial centers rather than at the
place of production,[2] and by comparing the prices
gathered in the provincial centers with those
paid directly to the producers by the Soil Products Office (whose function it is to stabilize
or maintain prices of cereals) in years when
this agency was engaged in large-scale purchases
of wheat and barley, the National Income Committe
of the Central Statistical Office estimates that
prices at the place of production for these products have been that much lower.[3]

(b) Prices of sugar beets
    The sugar beet price used is the one sent
to the author by the Turkish Sugar Company for
1952, which includes the value of the sugar prem-
ium paid by the company for their sugar purchases.
These prices are weighted averages as they are
derived by dividing the total paid for beets plus
the total value of the sugar premiums by the
total quantity of beet purchases. No reduction

was made in these prices as the Sugar Company
buys the beets directly from the producers, so
that these are the prices paid at the place of
production.

(3) <u>Yields</u>. The Mechanization Study
gives two sets of figures for mechanized and unmechanized agriculture, those reported by the
village heads (for wheat, barley, cotton, and
sugar beets respectively),[4] and those reported
by the sample farmers.[5] These two sets of data
vary somewhat. The village heads' reports are
almost consistently higher. It is the figures
supplied by the village heads that are used in
these calculations as it is believed that the information supplied by the village heads is probably more accurate than that supplied by the
farmers themselves, because the latter may have
tried to under-report. As noted earlier, one
always suspects this possibility in dealing with
information supplied by individuals that may disclose their own income or wealth.

Insofar as the average <u>increase</u> in yields
due to mechanization is concerned, it makes
little difference which set of figures is used
since the average increase turns out to be almost the same when calculated on the basis of
the data reported by the village heads or the
farm families; according to the village heads
mechanization increased yields by 34 percent
while the same figure based on the family reports is 35 percent.[6] The reason for the relatively small difference is in part due to the
fact that the farm families indicate lower yields
<u>both</u> from mechanized and unmechanized operations.
However, the increase in yields based on village
head data would have been higher had it not been
for the relatively low mechanized yields reported by the village heads for the southeastern
region which pulls down the average and which
probably results in an under-statement of the
typical increase.

B. Income Earned by Working Other Farmers' Land
    with Tractors for Pay

        The income earned by working other farm-
ers' land with tractors for pay was calculated as
follows: The Mechanization Study gives the total
number of decares in each region that are so
worked.[7] The income earned is TL. 3 per decare
for cultivation and 10-12 percent of the value
of the crop for harvesting.[8] It was assumed
that on the average both operations are performed
for wheat and barley, but that cotton and beets
are not harvested mechanically so that in the
case of the two latter crops the operations performed for others for pay consist only of cultivating the land with tractors but not of harvesting the crop.
        To calculate the return from harvesting
wheat and barley, certain assumptions had to be
made as to the products grown by the farmers for
whom this service was performed. For this purpose it was assumed that in each region the farmers who rent the services of tractors cultivate
the same crops and obtain the same high mechanized yields as the sample farmers in the same
region in the Mechanization Study.
        From the gross income from cultivating
and harvesting land for others, fuel costs had
to be deducted. The fuel costs per decare for
each region are estimated in section IIC below.
These figures were then multiplied by the area
cultivated for others in each region to cotton
and beets and to wheat and barley. In the case
of the former two crops this product gave the
fuel costs. In the case of the latter two crops
the fuel costs per decare were doubled to allow
for the fact that this land is worked twice, once
for cultivation and one for harvesting.

C. Savings in the Cost of Labor and Draft
    Animals

        Of these savings one can only make the

roughest estimates. One man with a pair of oxen is reported to be able to plow, seed, and work the seed into the ground on about one decare of wheat land a day in Central Anatolia.[9] This work has to be done between the beginning of the fall rains and the setting in of frost which allows for about forty-five working days. This means that one man with a pair of oxen can cultivate forty-five decares. One man with a tractor, on the other hand, cultivates an average of over 460 decares of land in the Mechanization Study,[10] or ten times as much. Therefore each tractor would save the wages of nine men (ten men minus the tractor driver) and of twenty work animals, although the saving in wages would be slightly offset by the higher wages paid the tractor drivers.

The saving in wages paid the ten men may be estimated by figuring forty-five days work in the fall for seeding and another thirty days' work in the spring for the second plowing and the plowing of the fallow.[11] If one uses a daily wage of TL. 3,[12] or TL. 225 per worker for seventy-five days' work, one obtains a total wage bill of TL. 2,250 for the ten men. From this must be deducted the wages of the tractor driver of TL. 408.[13] This leaves a net saving of labor of about TL. 1,842 per tractor and for 3,836 tractors used by the farmers in the Mechanization Study, this makes a total saving of TL. 7,066,000 for plowing the soil alone, as the seventy-five days' work figured above do not include the harvest season. If the crop is also harvested mechanically, the saving would be larger.

The savings in work-animal costs can be figured by taking each ox to cost TL. 20 worth of feed[14] and TL. 3.50 of animal shoes.[15] For twenty animals and 3,836 tractors this is a saving of TL. 1,803,000. This figure does not include any other saving in animal costs, such as shelter, vaccination, etc.

The sum of the savings in labor and animals figured above amounts to TL. 8,869,000. However the mechanized farmers in Turkey do not seem to effect all the savings in labor and animals that they might.[16] Assuming that they effect one half of the savings they might,[17] the savings would be TL. 4,435,000. This, although very rough, is likely to be conservative, especially as savings in harvest wages when the crop is harvested mechanically have not been included.

II. Cost of Equipment

From the increase in gross incomes the costs of tractors have to be deducted. These consist of (1) annual depreciation, (2) annual cost of repair of machinery and (3) fuel costs. Interest is not included among these costs because the return to be estimated is the return to all capital, both owned and borrowed.

A. Depreciation

Depreciation cost of tractors and other farm equipment was figured as follows: The total investment in farm equipment is given in the Mechanization Study in Table 105,[18] but this figure includes interest as well as value of investment. Interest, therefore, had to be deducted.

The total amount of borrowed funds is given in Table 107. As 95 percent of the farmers in the Mechanization Study who borrowed obtained their loans from the Agricultural Bank,[19] the Bank rate of 3 percent[20] was taken to be the rate of interest paid. Three percent of the borrowed funds were, therefore, considered to be interest, and when deducted from the "total investment plus interest," the residual gave the estimated value of investment alone. Depreciation was then taken to be 12.5 percent of the remainder.[21]

B.   Annual Cost of Repair of Farm Machinery

Table 51 of the Mechanization Study gives the annual cost of repair of all machinery per tractor and per year. The total cost for each region was calculated by multiplying the cost per tractor by the number of tractors in each region given in the Mechanization Study in Table 55.

C.   Fuel Costs

Fuel costs are not given in the Mechanization Study. However, I obtained estimates for 1956 from Nafiz Erus (at the time Head of the Agricultural Section of the Central Statistical Office). I then adjusted these figures to apply to 1952.

Mr. Erus' estimates were as follows: For one decare of land the fuel cost, when gasoline is used, is 3 kg. of gasoline in 1956, plus TL. 0.10 for lubrication and TL. 0.10 for grease. When diesel oil is used, the cost is 2 kg. of diesel oil, plus the same cost for lubrication and grease as when gasoline is used. When kerosene is used, the cost of fuel is about 10 percent less than when diesel oil is used, while the cost of lubrication and grease is the same.

With this information it was possible to estimate the 1952 costs in the following manner: In 1952 wholesale prices of gasoline, diesel oil, and kerosene are given in Konjonktur.[22] The prices of lubricants and oil are not given, but it was assumed that their prices changed as much as the average price of fuels. On the basis of these data the total cost per decare, in 1952, of fuel, lubrication, and grease, when different fuels are used, was estimated. These costs were then weighted by the relative number of families in each region who answered in the study that they used gasoline, diesel oil, or kerosene[23] to find the average cost per decare for each region. The total fuel cost for crop land in each region

could be determined by multiplying these costs
by the total number of decares cultivated with
tractors in these regions, and by doubling the
resulting figures to allow for double plowing.

In addition to the fuel cost for crop
land, an estimate had to be made of the cost of
working the fallow land with tractors. For this
purpose the amount of fallow land first had to
be estimated. The information on area cultivated in the Mechanization Study only refers to
crop land, and thus the amount of fallow land
had to be obtained from independent data for
each region.

Agricultural Structure and Production,
1946-1953, pages 3-4, gives for 1952 the area
sown and the area fallow for nine regions.
From these data the ratio of fallow land to land
sown was calculated for each of the regions included in the Mechanization Study, and the average amount of fallow land of the farms in the
Mechanization Study in each region was estimated by adding the same proportion of fallow land
to the area cultivated as the proportion of fallow land is to crop land in the region. By applying these regional averages to the farms in
the Mechanization Study, the assumption is made
that the land of the mechanized farmers is of
about average quality in the region so far as
rainfall is concerned, and that irrigation did
not have a significant effect in reducing the
area of fallow land. As the fallow land is
cultivated once, this area was then multiplied
once by the fuel cost per decare in the region.

III. Net Income per Farm from Investment in
Modern Equipment in the Mechanization Study,
and Rate of Return on the Investment

A. Weights Used to Average the Regional Data

The regional income and cost calculations made above are summarized in Table 1 (see

page 199), columns (1) to (6). In column (7)
the regional totals are averaged, and in column (8) they are converted into average incomes
and costs per farm. Line 9 shows that the average net increase in income due to tractors was
TL. 4,396 thousand per region, or TL. 8,737 per
farm. The regional data were averaged rather
than added because the number of mechanized
farms in each region included in the Mechanization Study sample is not as representative of
the relative importance of mechanized farms by
regions as it should be. Therefore some method
had to be devised to calculate a weighted regional average, in which the weights chosen for
each region would correct for the geographical
over-and under-representation of mechanized
farms in the sample. (To make the averages more
meaningful the average regional totals were also converted into averages per farm.) As the
relative importance of mechanized farms in different regions can be represented by the relative area cultivated with tractors in each region, to derive the new weights, this area had
to be estimated.

The average number of decares that a
tractor cultivates in each region was calculated
from the Mechanization Study. This average varies greatly from region to region and this had to
be taken into account in deriving the new weights.[24]
These figures were then multiplied by the actual
total number of tractors in each region which are
published by the Central Statistical Office and the
resulting area cultivated with tractors (area per
tractor times number of tractors) in each region,[25]
taken as a percent of the total area cultivated
with tractors in the nation, gave the new weights.

B. The Rate of Return

To calculate the rate of return, the
value of the investment from which this income
is derived must be calculated. The income calculated above does not only refer to the earn-

TABLE 1

RATE OF RETURN ON INVESTMENT IN TRACTORS AND MODERN EQUIPMENT OF THE FARMERS IN THE MECHANIZATION STUDY: SUMMARY OF CALCULATIONS

| | Regional totals (in thousands of TL.) | | | | | | Weighted average of regional totals (7) | Weighted average per farm (in TL.)f (8) |
	Central Anatolia (1)	Mediterranean (2)	Aegean (3)	Marmara (4)	South East Anatolia (5)	Black Sea (6)		
Gross Income								
1. Increase in gross income due to increased yields	4,085	11,668	9,443	1,324	2,168	153	5,921	11,771
2. Income earned from working land for others for pay	407	272	101	190	88	39	247	489
3. TOTAL increase in income	4,492	11,940	9,544	1,514	2,256	192	6,168	12,260
Costs								
4. Depreciation	1,181	1,822	1,334	698	623	197	1,188	2,363
5. Repair	364	843	517	162	456	49	509	1,011
6. Fuel	692	1,096	431	171	1,055	14	814	1,619
7. TOTAL cost	2,237	3,761	2,282	1,031	2,134	260	2,511	4,993
8. Savings in costs a							739	1,470
9. Net income b							4,396	8,737
Value of investment								
10. New value	9,447	14,575	10,675	5,587	4,986	1,578	9,508	18,903
11. Depreciation to 1952 c	-	-	-	-	-	-	1,696	3,370
12. New value less depreciation d	-	-	-	-	-	-	7,812	15,533
13. Rate of return on investment e	-	-	-	-	-	-	56%	56%

a. In Section IC, in the text above the total savings
    in the cost of labor and draft animals had been esti-
    mated at TL. 4,435,000 for all the farms in the Mech-
    anization Study. In column (7) above this figure has
    been divided by 6 to get the regional average, and in
    column (8) by 3,015 (the number of farms included in
    the Mechanization Study survey) to derive the average
    per farm.

b. Line 3 minus line 7, plus line 8.

c. The present value of the tractors and equipment owned
    by the farmers in the Mechanization Study is estimated
    to be 17.8% less than the new value. The figures
    TL. 1,696,000 and TL. 3,370 in the table above are
    17.8% of the average new value of the investment of
    TL. 9,508,000 per region and of TL. 18,903 per farm.
        The rate of 17.8% is derived as follows: Table 24
    in the Mechanization Study shows the number of tractors
    owned by the farmers in the study during the years
    1948 to 1952. From this table one can calculate the
    age of the tractors owned, and by taking the yearly
    depreciation to be 12.5%, the proportion of the value
    of tractors that should have depreciated by 1952.
    This proportion is 18.8%.
        If one assumes that the equipment is of the same
    age as the tractors, but takes the rate of deprecia-
    tion of equipment to be 10%, one arrives at 15.0% total
    depreciation of equipment. Since tractors account for
    74.6% of the value of all modern equipment owned by
    the farmers in the Mechanization Study (from Mechaniza-
    Study, Table 111), and other equipment for 25.4%, by
    taking 18.8% of 74.6% of the total investment of
    TL. 18,903 above, and 15% of the other 25.4%, one
    obtains an average depreciation of 17.8% for tractors
    and equipment combined.

d. Line 11 subtracted from line 10.

e. Line 9 as percent of line 12.

f. The weighted average data per farm were derived from
    the regional averages in column (7) by dividing the
    data in column (7) by 503. (503 is the average num-
    ber of farms included in the Mechanization Study sur-
    vey per region. The total number of farms included
    in the survey was 3,015, and 6 regions were covered.

ings of tractors, but includes the earnings
from other modern equipment as well, such as
tractor plows, mechanical threshers, etc. Therefore this income must be ascribed to all modern
equipment owned by the farmers in the Mechanization Study, of which tractors amount to only
74.6 percent in value.[26] The value of the investment in all modern equipment owned by the
farmers in the Mechanization Study is shown and
averaged in Table 1, line 10. On a per farm
basis the average new value of this equipment is
TL. 18,903. From this depreciation to 1952 must
be deducted, which is estimated to be 17.8 percent of the new value, or TL. 3,370 per farm
(line 11). This leaves a present worth of
TL. 15,533 (line 12). Since the net income from
tractors and modern equipment is estimated to be
TL. 8,737 (line 9) one gets a rate of return of
56 percent (line 13).

  This rate is likely to be lower than the
actual one for the following reasons:

  1. Omitted from the increased income
due to tractors calculated above are savings in
seed when drills are used in planting small
grains. Reşat Aktan estimates this saving to
amount to at least 25 percent in seed.[27] While
most other equipment contributed to increasing
yields and is thus included in the estimate above,
drills do not affect yields and their effect is
thus not included.

  2. As stated above, the potential savings in labor costs are calculated on the assumption that the crops are not harvested mechanically,
and even though only half of the potential saving was included in the estimate, the <u>potential</u>
saving itself is likely to be larger because
some crops are harvested with tractors. The possible savings in harvest wages were omitted because it could not be ascertained to what extent
these crops were harvested mechanically.

  Although the object of these calculations is to find the rate of return on the total
investment in tractors, whether the funds for

this investment were borrowed or not, it should be noted that the rate of return obtained by the tractor owners on their equity capital is considerably larger. Table 108 in the Mechanization Study shows that these farmers invested on the average only 40 percent and borrowed 60 percent of the funds needed to buy the tractors and related equipment. Since most of them borrowed from the Agricultural Bank at the negligible interest rate of 3 percent, the average rate of return to tractor owners on their equity capital was not 56 percent, but nearly two and a half times this rate, or 136 percent.[28]

APPENDIX C

THE RATE OF RETURN FROM INVESTMENTS IN
NON-WORK ANIMALS AND THEIR
ANIMAL BUILDINGS IN TURKEY

To derive the functional distribution of agricultural incomes in Part I of this book, it is
necessary to estimate the income farmers obtain
from various types of investment as a rate of
return. The object of this appendix is to find
the rate of return on the investment in non-
work animals and their buildings. Since two sets
of data are available for deriving this rate--
(1) the Turkish national income data and related
statistics of the Central Statistical Office on
which the estimates of national income are based,
and (2) the Village Study--two independent estimates of this rate of return will be made, and
the results of the two estimates will be compared
in the end. As will be seen, this comparison
will point to serious over-estimates of the
value of the agricultural income derived from
animals in the national income statistics.

I. The Rate of Return from Investments
in Non-Work Animals Based on
National Income Data

The rate based on national income data
is derived by estimating (a) the value of the investments in non-work animals, (b) the value of
investments in animal buildings, and (c) the net
income derived from animals and animal products.
In the end the net income is expressed as a percent of the total investment to obtain the rate
of return.

A. The Value of Investments in Non-Work Animals

By multiplying the number of animals by

their prices in provincial centers it is possible
to estimate the value of the stock of animals in
1950 at 1951 prices. The value of animals
arrived at in this manner was reduced by 20 percent as the National Income Committee of the
Central Statistical Office estimates that the
prices at the farm are that much lower than in
provincial centers.[1] Since the resulting figure
gave the value of the stock of animals in 1950
at 1951 prices, this figure was then raised 8.6
percent to allow for the increase in livestock
numbers between 1950 and 1951.[2] This gave an investment in 1951 of TL. 1,827 million, as shown
in Table 1 (see page 205).

B.   The Value of Investments in Livestock Build-
     ings

        To the value of investments in animals
has to be added the value of the investments in
livestock buildings estimated at TL. 112 million.[3]
        The total value of the investment in
non-work animals and their buildings is therefore
TL. 1,827 million, plus TL. 113 million, or a
total of TL. 1,940 million.

C.   The Income from Non-Work Animals

        (1) The net income without deductions
for factor costs. A figure for the estimated income from non-work animals is given in the national income figures where the net income from
animals and animal products is put at TL. 1,727
million in 1951.[4] This figure requires adjustment, however, because the animal costs that are
deducted to derive the net figure include the
cost of work animals, and for present purposes
expenditures for work animals should be considered a cost of crops. The function of work animals is similar to that of agricultural machinery, their contribution consisting of work power
rather than of animal products, so that their
cost should not be charged to animal products
which they do not produce.

TABLE 1

ESTIMATE OF THE VALUE OF NON-WORK ANIMALS IN 1951
(In millions of TL.)

Value of the stock of non-work animals in 1950 at 1951 prices[a]	2,103
Minus: 20% of this value[b]	- 421
Equals: Estimated value of the stock of non-work animals in 1950 at 1951 prices	=1,682
Plus: Increase in the stock of non-work animals between 1950 and 1951 (8.6%)[c]	+ 145
Equals: Estimated value of the stock of non-work animals in 1951	=1,827

a. Derived by multiplying the number of each type of non-work animal in cities and villages by the prices of these animals in provincial centers. For these computations the stock of non-work animals was taken to include sheep, goats, Angora goats, as well as cattle and buffalos that are not used for draft purposes, and poultry. For the larger animals these computations were done separately for males, females and young animals.

The prices for all animals other than poultry were obtained directly from the Central Statistical Office, as they are not published for all animals. The prices of poultry are given in Agricultural Structure and Production, 1946-1953, p. 6.

The number of animals was derived from 1950 Agricultural Census Results, p. 4, Monthly Bulletin of Statistics, No. 34-36, p. 176, and 1950 Agricultural Census Results, p. 2.

An explanation is required of the derivation of the number of the larger non-work animals (cattle, buffalos, etc.). A question arose as to their actual number because it is not clear whether the data on "(number of) livestock" in the 1950 Agricultural Census Results include the work animals or not. Closer analysis, however, shows that work animals are included with the "(number of) livestock." This could be established by comparing the data in the 1950 Agricultural

Census Results, pp. 2 and 4, with similar statistics in Monthly Bulletin of Statistics, No. 34-36, p. 177, and Turkey, Central Statistical Office, 1948 Village Census Summary Results (Publication No. 320; Ankara: Central Statistical Office, 1952), p. 3.

b. The National Income Committee of the Central Statistical Office estimates that prices in provincial centers for animals have to be reduced by 20% to arrive at the value of animals at the farm. (Türkiye Millî Geliri, Appendix Table 46.)

c. The change in the stock of non-work animals between 1950 and 1951 is derived by calculating the percentage change in the number of each type of animal between 1950 and 1951, shown in the Monthly Bulletin of Statistics, No. 64, p. 143, and by then applying these percentage changes to the value of each of these types of animals calculated for 1950.

The animal costs that should be assigned to crops are 1. the cost due to loss and depreciation of draft animals of TL. 120 million, and 2. 60 percent of all remaining costs. The proportion of 60 percent is derived from a comparison of the costs of work and non-work animals estimated in Appendix A above for the farmers in the Village Study, or TL. 193 million.[5] The total overstatement in the costs of non-work animals is, therefore, TL. 313 million. This gives a net income from animals of TL. 2,040 million (TL. 1,727 million plus TL. 313 million), compared to a gross income of TL. 2,169 million.

(2) <u>Deduction of factor costs other than the return on investment</u>. The figure of TL. 2,040 million is net only of costs considered for national income calculations. The return on the investment in animals to the owners of these animals is smaller, as national income figures do not deduct costs that are incomes to factors of production, and in this instance do not count wages and rent as costs.

One can calculate from the Village Study data that paid shepherd wages for tending non-work animals amount to 4 percent of the net factor incomes derived from animals and animal products.[6] Since imputed shepherd wages should be negligible,[7] the marginal product of shepherd labor in the nation comes to approximately TL. 82 million.[8] If this figure is deducted from TL. 2,040 million, one is left with TL. 1,958 million for the net income clear of wage costs, i.e., for the factor returns to capital and land.

The return to land presents somewhat of a problem. It was noted in Chapter V that pasture land should theoretically be considered a free good. Since few legal or customary limits seem to be placed on the number of animals pastured, or on conversion of pastures into crop land, the number of animals should increase, or the amount of pasture land decline, until diminishing returns on the pasture land reduce imputed rent to zero, i.e., until the return on the investment in livestock is no higher than the return on other types of agricultural investment. It was noted in Chapter V that this process had already gone quite far, but that some imputed rent on pasture land was probably still left in 1951. Since the amount of this rent cannot be estimated, the figure of TL. 1,958 million, while primarily constituting a return to capital, is also likely to include some imputed rent.

The rate of return on non-work animals derived from the national income data is just about 100 percent (the net income is TL. 1,958 million and the total value of the investment in non-work animals and buildings TL. 1,940 million). Even though this figure is likely to include some imputed rent, it seems extremely large.

II.   The Rate of Return from Investments in Non-Work Animals Based on the Village Study

One can check the result derived from the national income statistics against the rate of return calculated from the data in the Village Study. For this purpose it is necessary to estimate the value of investments in non-work animals and in animal buildings owned by the farmers in the Village Study.

A.   Value of Investments in Non-Work Animals

The Village Study contains data on the total value of all animals owned by the farmers in each land bracket,[9] but not on the value of work and non-work animals separately. However, the value of non-work animals could be computed separately from the Village Study data on the number of each kind of animal owned by the farmers in every land bracket[10] and their prices.[11]

Although only the value of non-work animals is needed, the value of work animals was also computed (by the same method), to test the results. The test consisted of comparing the sum of the computed values for work and non-work animals with the total actual value of both types of animals in the Village Study, since the study gives these values only for both types of animals combined. This comparison could be made separately for each land bracket. The test showed that the difference between the actual total and computed total values was 8 percent for the lowest land bracket, 1, 4, and 10 percent for the succeeding ones, and 4 percent on the average.[12] This indicated a remarkable degree of consistency between the computed and actual data, and the computed values for non-work animals could be taken to be a fairly good approximation of the actual values of these animals in the Village Study.

B. Value of Investments in Buildings

The value of investments in buildings could be derived from the expenditures on depreciation and repair of buildings estimated in Appendix A above for non-work animals.[13] In the national income statistics these expenditures constitute about 40 percent of the value of buildings,[14] and from this information the value of the buildings could be computed for each land bracket.[15]

A word of caution must be added about these estimates. The Village Study does not actually give data on depreciation and repair of buildings. Instead the farmers were asked to supply information on expenditures on construction and repair of buildings, which, in an average year, might approximate the value of depreciation and repair.[16] But 1953, the year to which the data in the Village Study refer, was an unusually good crop year which was, moreover, preceded by two other good crop years. Under these circumstances it is very likely that construction activity in 1953 was greater than mere replacement and repair of buildings, but there are no data to correct for this overstatement. Therefore the rate of return on investments for the Village Study should be somewhat larger than the one estimated below, since this rate should be taken as a percentage of a somewhat smaller total value of investments. The extent of the overestimate should be small, however, since value of animal buildings is small relative to the value of the livestock itself.[17]

C. The Rate of Return from Non-Work Animals in the Village Study

The net income derived from non-work animals is estimated in Appendix A above, Table 3. This return, taken as a percent of the estimated value of the investment from which it is derived, gives the rate of return earned on investments. The pertinent data are shown in Table 2 (see page 211). The table shows that the rate of return on investments in non-work animals in the Village Study varies between 33 and 35 percent, the average being 34 percent. As in the case of the estimates based on the national income data, the rate of return includes some imputed rent.

III. Comparison of the Two Rates Derived

The two rates of return, derived first from the official data and then for the farmers in the Village Study, are completely different. In the one case the rate is about 100 percent, and in the second 34 percent. Why this difference?

A. Reasons for the Difference between the Two Rates

The difference does not seem to lie in

TABLE 2

DERIVATION OF THE RATE OF RETURN FROM INVESTMENTS
IN NON-WORK ANIMALS IN THE VILLAGE STUDY,
BY LAND BRACKETS
(In TL.)

		Farms by land-size brackets (decares)				
		10-79 (1)	80-159 (2)	160-499 (3)	500 and over (4)	Average all farms[c] (5)
1.	Net return from non-work animals[a]	258	388	775	1,916	340
2.	Value of investment in non-work animals and their buildings	756	1,187	2,267	5,460	999
3.	Net rate of return from investment in non-work animals and their buildings[b]	34%	33%	34%	35%	34%

a. Estimated in Appendix A, Table 3.

b. Line 2 as percent of line 3.

c. The average is weighted according to the relative number of farms in each land bracket in the nation rather than the relative number in the Village Study in which the sample includes too many large farms.

the number of animals from which these incomes
are derived. A test of consilience of the number of animals per farm in the Village Study with
those reported in the 1950 Census of Agriculture
for the regions surveyed in the Village Study--
roughly agricultural regions I and IX--shows a
fairly good agreement, as shown in Table 3,[18]
(see page 213), although for the smaller animals
there is not so much agreement in detail as in
overall numbers.

It is true that in Table 3 the Village
Study data refer to 1953, while those for regions
I and IX refer to 1950, and that according to
the official data livestock numbers increased
during this three-year interval. Assuming,
however, that the number of farms increased in
proportion to the increase in the rural population between 1950 and 1953, the increase in
livestock numbers per farm was not great enough
to alter the general agreement in these numbers
shown in Table 3.[19]

Not only do the data on number of livestock from which these two rates of return are
derived agree reasonably well, but so do the price
data, as the prices used to calculate the value
of animals in the national income accounts had
been found to coincide with the prices implicit
in the data on animal values in the Village
Study. (It will be recalled that when the number of animals in the Village Study was multiplied by these prices, the resulting values came
out to be very close to the actual ones reported
in the Village Study.)

Since the difference between the two
rates of return derived is not due to inconsis-
tencies between the number or value of animals
in the official data and in the Village Study,
the difference between the two rates must derive from differences in the amount of income
estimated to have been earned from them. The
question therefore arises: which of the two
sets of data on animal incomes, those in the
national income estimates or those in the Vil-

TABLE 3

NUMBER OF ANIMALS PER FARM IN THE VILLAGE STUDY
AND IN AGRICULTURAL REGIONS I AND IX

	Village Study[a]	Regions I and IX[b]
Cattle[c]	3.75	3.57
Buffalos[c]	0.38	0.35
Sheep, goats, and Angora goats	18.35	18.74
- sheep	(12.82)	(11.44)
- goats	(3.56)	(2.66)
- Angora goats	(1.97)	(4.64)

a. From Village Study, Table 16. To arrive at the av-
    erage for all farms the farms in each land bracket were
    weighted by the total number of farms of each size in
    the nation, rather than the number in the Village
    Study where the large farms seem to be over-represen-
    ted.

b. From 1950 Agricultural Census Results, pp. 2-5. The
    total number of each kind of animal in villages with-
    out distinction for sex and age (shown on pp. 2-5),
    was divided by the total number of families in villages
    reporting land (shown on pp. 2-3). Each of these num-
    bers would have been 8% smaller (i.e., 92% of those
    shown in this table) if the number of animals had been
    divided by the number of families in villages that re-
    ported land plus those who did not report land.

c. Includes cattle and buffalos used as work animals.

lage Study, is the more reliable one? The accuracy of the national income estimates is considered first.

B. The Accuracy of the National Income Data on Animal Incomes

The national income statistics for the output of animals and animal products is derived by means of formulas because data concerning the number of animals produced and consumed on farms, i.e., the greater part of the output of animals, are not available. To fill this gap the National Income Committee used formulas based on the number of offspring a herd of 100 females could be expected to produce in a year, and how many would be expected to die a natural death. The formulas are those used in some European countries, although they were modified somewhat to make them applicable to Turkish conditions.[20]

These formulas seem to have assumed rather ideal conditions. It was assumed, for example, that each milk-cow has one offspring a year, a theoretical possibility, but one that does not necessarily take place in reality.[21] A more serious criticism of the estimates, however, derives from the fact that the formulas were not modified in subsequent years, or not sufficiently so, to take account of the fact that by the early 1950's grazing land should have given rise to severe diminishing returns. Thus in 1951 a group of experts expressed the view that increases in the output of animal products were not expected to come about through further increases in the animal population,[22] a statement that implied that there were severe diminishing returns in the output of animal products. The reasons for these developments were explained on pp. 63-69 above. In the national income estimates, however, no account is taken of the fact that the output per animal should have declined as a result of diminishing returns; instead, for

the ten-year period 1948 to 1958 for which separate data on the value of animal products in the
national income statistics could be obtained,
this value, in constant prices, increased even
faster than the number of animals who produce
these products in the official data.[23] There is
no question, therefore, that the income from animal products in the national income statistics
is overestimated.[24]

C. Evaluation of the Accuracy of Animal Data in
    the Village Study

         How accurate are the animal data in the
Village Study? One can have a reasonable measure
of confidence in the Village Study data because
of the high degree of internal consistency ex-
hibited by the animal data in the study. Thus,
the rates of return estimated from the Village
Study data are very similar for each of the four
land brackets, suggesting that the data supplied
by the farmers in each one of the land brackets
in the Village Study are consistent with those
supplied by those in each of the other land
brackets. For example, it is impressive that
the rates of return calculated for the various
land brackets (shown in Table 2 on p. 180) varied
by only 2 percent between different brackets,
the lowest being 33 percent for the second-highest land bracket, and the highest 35 percent for
the highest bracket. This, together with the
fact that the number of animals shown in the
Village Study is so remarkably consistent with
the data on the total value of investments in
animals given in the Village Study (see pp. 208-
09), increases one's confidence in the fact that
the data reported by these farmers concerning
animals are fairly accurate.

D.   Conclusion:
     The Rate of Return on Investments in Non-
     Work Animals in Turkey

        Since the data on animal incomes in the
Village Study appear to be quite good, while
those in the national income estimates are definitely too large, the rate of return on investments in animals of 34 percent derived from the
Village Study will be used in preference to that
of 100 percent derived from the national income
data.

ANALYSIS OF THE SHARE OF DIFFERENT FACTORS
RESPONSIBLE FOR THE HIGHER INCOMES
PER DECARE OF MECHANIZED FARMERS
COMPARED WITH AVERAGE FARMERS
IN THE SAME REGION

It is possible to estimate to what extent the
farmers in the Mechanization Study obtained higher incomes per decare than the average farmer in
their regions and what share of this income was
caused by (1) changed yields due to mechanization, (2) types of crops grown, and (3) other
factors affecting yields. The effects of these
factors could be isolated by recalculating the
income of the mechanized farmers several times
in such a manner that in each of these calculations all variables are constant except the one
whose effect on the magnitude of the incomes of
the mechanized farmers one wants to estimate.
The results are shown in Table 1 (see page 218).
Table 1 shows the following relationships:
1. The difference between columns (1)
and (2) is due to the types of crops grown,
i.e., the fact that, on the average, the four
main crops grown by the farmers in the Mechanization Study give them a higher income per
decare than the average income per decare obtained by all farmers in the same provinces from
all their crops. Between these two columns the
yields and the prices are constant for those
crops that are the same in both columns. Only
the types of crops or their relative importance
differ.[1]
2. The data in column (2) compared to
column (3) measure the difference between the
yields from unmechanized agriculture reported in
the Mechanization Study, and the average yields
obtained for the same crops in the region. Between these two columns the types of crops grown

TABLE 1

ANALYSIS OF THE DEGREE TO WHICH THE GROSS INCOMES PER DECARE OF
MECHANIZED FARMERS ARE HIGHER THAN THOSE OF UNMECHANIZED
FARMERS BECAUSE OF DIFFERENCES IN TYPES OF
CROPS GROWN, AND BECAUSE OF DIFFERENCES
IN YIELDS OBTAINED FROM MECHANIZED
AND UNMECHANIZED AGRICULTURE
(In TL.)

Regions	Average income per decare in each region from all crops	Income per decare of the farmers in the Mechanization Study from their four crops		
		assuming that they obtained the average yields in their region[d]	assuming that their yields were those of unmechanized agriculture[c]	With mechanized yields[b]
	(1)	(2)	(3)	(4)
1. Central Anatolia	20.4	15.9	18.5	24.8
2. Mediterranean	45.5	61.7	48.9	70.7
3. Aegean	54.2	102.7	110.7	159.2
4. Marmara	32.7	28.0	29.0	37.5
5. South East Anatolia	22.0	18.6	16.6	19.3
6. Black Sea	37.7	31.0	28.0	40.1
7. Average[e]	25.8	36.3	36.5	50.6
Comparison of averages				
8. Index, col. (1) = 100	100	141	141	196
9. Index, col. (2) = 100		100	101	130
10. Index, col. (3) = 100			100	139

a. These data are computed as explained in Chapter VI, Table 2, note a, ex-
    cept that here they are classified by regions rather than provinces. The
    provinces included in each region are those included in the Mechanization
    Study to make the data comparable with the regional averages in the other
    columns which are based on the classification in the Mechanization Study.
        The data by provinces are not adjusted for any overstatement in cereal
    yields in the official data. However the average in line 7 was reduced 9%
    to adjust for these overestimates. The proportion of 9% was used because
    44% of the income of the farmers in the Mechanization Study (if calculated
    with either mechanized or unmechanized yields reported by farmers) derives
    from cereals, and in the official statistics cereal yields are on the av-
    erage about 20% too high.

b. The estimated total gross income of the farmers in the Mechanization Study
    from their four main crops (no information on the other crops is given in
    the study), which takes account of the high yields they obtained from
    their mechanized operations, divided by the estimated area sown to these

crops. The method of estimating their total gross income is explained on pp. 189-92 of Appendix B.

As mentioned above, the income per decare was found by dividing the estimated total income of the mechanized farmers by the estimated area sown to these crops. How the total income was derived is indicated in the paragraph above. The total area was calculated by increasing the area in the Mechanization Study (Table 59) by the proportion that fallow land is to all crop land in the provinces in which sample farmers were located in the Mechanization Study. The proportion of fallow land is derived from data in Agricultural Structure and Production, 1946-1953, pp. 3-4, where total crop land is taken to be the sum of: area sown, fallow land, orchards and gardens, olive groves.

c. Same as note (b) above, except that to derive the gross income of the mechanized farmers from these four crops it was assumed that, in this instance, they obtained only the yields shown in the Mechanization Study from their crops for unmechanized agriculture. These yields are shown in Chapter VI, Table 4.

d. Same as note (b) above, except that to derive the gross income of mechanized farmers it was assumed this time that the yields they obtained for their four crops was the average yield of each of these crops obtained in the provinces in which they are located. The average yield was derived by dividing the total output in the provinces in which sample farmers were located in each of the six regions in the Mechanization Study by the total area planted to the crops in these provinces. The data were taken from Agricultural Structure and Production, 1946-1954, pp. 34-161.

No adjustment was made in lines 1-6 for the overestimate in cereal yields reported in the official data; but the average in line 7 was reduced 5.7% as cereals constitute 28% of the value of output in column (2), and the cereal portion of this output should be reduced 20% to correct for overestimates.

e. To derive the average in line 7 the regional weights were calculated, as explained in Appendix B, note 25 and pp. 197-98 as the weights implicit in the Mechanization Study sample are not as representative as they should be. The index in line 8 (and therefore also those in lines 9 and 10), turned out, however, to be hardly different whether the weights implicit in the Mechanization Study data were used, or those calculated in Appendix B. With Mechanization Study weights all the averages were slightly higher, but the <u>degree</u> to which they varied was almost identical. For adjustments in the averages in columns (1) and (2), see also notes a and d.

f. Although the index numbers in line 8, columns 2 and 3, appear identical, there is a difference of about ½ of one percent, which was rounded off. This small difference, when rounded too, appears as a 1% discrepancy in line 9.

are constant, and so is the area planted to each crop and their prices. Only the yields are different.

3. The difference between columns (3) and (4) is due to higher mechanized yields obtained by the farmers in the Mechanization Study if they had been fully mechanized, compared to the yields obtained from unmechanized agriculture as reported in that study. The types of crops again are constant, as well as the area planted to each, and their prices. Only the yields are different.

By comparing the data in the table one comes to the following conclusions:

1. The income per decare in column (2) is 41 percent higher than in column (1), showing that the types of crops grown by the farmers in the Mechanization Study <u>alone</u> accounted for that much higher incomes per decare for these farmers.

2. The income per decare in column (3) is 1 percent higher than in column (2), indicating that the yield from unmechanized agriculture reported in the Mechanization Study is about the same as the average yield from the same crops in the region (from mechanized and unmechanized operations).

3. The income per decare in column (4) is 39 percent higher than in column (3), indicating that the farmers in the Mechanization Study got that much higher incomes only because the mechanized yields are that much higher than the yields from unmechanized agriculture.

4. The income per decare in column (4) compared to column (1) is 96 percent higher, showing that the combination of all these factors gives the farmers in the Mechanization Study that much higher incomes per decare than the average income per decare of these regions (where the average includes both mechanized and unmechanized operations).

APPENDIX E

TEST OF CONSILIENCE OF THE 1952 FALL SURVEY
ON THE DISTRIBUTION OF LAND OPERATED

As noted in Chapter I, the accuracy of statistics in Turkey cannot be taken for granted. Because of this, wherever possible, data used
should be tested for consistency or consilience
with other data independently derived. This applies particularly to the 1952 Fall Survey[1] on
the distribution of land operated, for the reliability of the estimates on income distribution by size derived in Part II (especially
Chapters VI-VIII) depends to a large extent on
the accuracy of the data gathered in this survey. The reason for this is that for the estimate of income distribution by size the distribution of land operated was taken as a point of
departure, but was subsequently modified to take
account of factors other than size of land operated that affect income distribution. It will
also be recalled that the distribution of income
that farmers derive from crops and animals bore
a considerable resemblance to the distribution
of land operated, and since farming is the main
source of income for farmers, even after the
revenue from other sources was taken into account, the final distribution still did not de-
part too greatly from that of land operated upon
which the estimates were originally based. Because the one single survey on the distribution
of land operated played such a basic role in the
estimates in Part II it is important to determine
whether the data on the distribution of land operated that were gathered in the 1952 Fall Survey are reasonably reliable.

To determine their reliability these
data will be subjected to two tests: (1) The
first examines whether the total of land operated as reported in the 1952 Fall Survey from
which the distribution of land operated is de-

rived agrees with the total of land cultivated
reported in Agricultural Structure and Production,
1946-1954, which is based on data gathered
independently by the Central Statistical Office.
If tree crops, vineyards, etc., are included,
the total of land cultivated should approximately
equal the total land operated since animals are
not generally grazed on farms. (2) Since the
basic data were derived via the sampling method
the representativeness of the sample will also
be tested, not only for the overall distribution,
but also for the distribution of land operated
by provinces, since the distribution of land operated for the country as a whole might appear
to represent the actual situation fairly well
only because biases in the provincial distributions tend to cancel out.

I.   Testing the Amount of Land Operated

        The data on the distribution of land op-
erated are based on information supplied by the
heads of rural households in a sample survey conducted by the Central Statistical Office. Because these statistics are derived from information supplied by the farmers themselves, there
arises the suspicion that they may have been
under-reported. As noted earlier, all those who
worked with statistical surveys in Turkey whom
the writer has consulted have expressed the view
that respondents tend to understate their holdings. The apparent reason for this is the wide-
spread fear of the tax collector and the belief
that data gathered for any purpose would ulti-
mately find their way to the tax collector's office and mean a larger tax bill. In the foreword
to the published results of the 1950 Census of
Agriculture, for example, one reads: "Understatement (or overstatement) bias on the part of
the respondents is often a major problem with
which to be reckoned..."[2] The parentheses in

this sentence as well as the comments made by statisticians indicate, however, that under-statement is the major problem.

To test the data for understatement, the total amount of land operated can be compared with data on the total amount of land cultivated in Agricultural Structure and Production, an independent estimate made every year by the Central Statistical Office. When this comparison is made, the two figures turn out to be remarkably alike. The total amount of land operated is 19,452,000 hectares,[3] and the amount of land cultivated is 19,148,749 hectares.[4] The comparison indicates that under-reporting has apparently not affected the accuracy of the over-all amount of land operated.[5]

II.   Testing the Regional Distribution of Land Operated

In making the estimate in Part II of this book not only was the general distribution of land operated used but also the sub-distributions for each province. It is therefore important to test whether the number of farms in all land brackets for each province is relatively accurate.

The distribution of land operated is based on a sample of 1/600 of all rural farm families,[6] and this raises the question whether the sample was large enough in relation to the universe to give representative results. For the over-all distribution test (1) has shown that the results seem to be acceptable. But there is also the question whether the distribution within the provinces is representative. Thus, even if the total number and total area of farms of all sizes is representative, one cannot conclude without further evidence that the location of the farms in each land bracket in high and low income provinces is also reasonably

accurate. Yet it is this location that determines to what extent the distribution of gross
incomes was more or less equal than the distribution of land operated. For example, if in the
sample all large farms are predominantly reported in the very high income provinces, the distribution of gross incomes would be more unequal
than if they were mostly found in the low income
provinces.

The main problem with respect to the size
of the sample concerns the location of large
farms. Their dispersion is very great, and with
a sample of 1/600 the sampling error could be
very great. In the case of the small farms,
their number in each province is relatively
large and with this small dispersion the sampling
error for these farms should be more moderate.
Table 1 (see page 226) shows the average number
of farms per province included in the sample in
each land bracket. For the farms in the two
largest land brackets, the average number is
only 1.1. This means that a sample of 1/600
could, by chance, completely miss all or include
too many of the farms of this size in a given
province.

When the large farms included in the
sample are then multiplied by 600 (since the
size of the sample was 1/600), these chance factors may be greatly magnified. As a result a
much larger number than the actual number of
large farms may be included in some provinces
and a much smaller in others, which in turn may
greatly distort the location of these farms in
high or low income provinces, and thus their
average income per decare.

There is some indication that this has
actually happened. It was noted in test (1)
that the total amount of land operated in the
sample is about equal to the total amount of
land cultivated in Turkey as reported in Agricultural Structure and Production. But when the
same comparison is made by provinces[7] sizeable
discrepancies between these two sets of figures

TABLE 1

AVERAGE NUMBER OF FARMS PER PROVINCE INCLUDED IN
EACH LAND BRACKET IN THE SAMPLE OF THE
DISTRIBUTION OF LAND OPERATED

Land brackets (decares) (1)	Average number of farms per province in the sample[a] (2)
0 - 20	21.1
20 - 50	21.8
50 - 75	9.2
75 - 100	5.9
100 - 150	4.6
150 - 200	2.5
200 - 300	1.9
300 - 500	1.1
500 - 700	.5
700 and over	.6
TOTAL	69.2

a. Computed by dividing the total number of farms in each land bracket in the distribution of land operated by 36,600, i.e., by 61 (the number of provinces included in the sample) and again by 600 (since the sample was 1/600).

226

appear.[8] Moreover in 62 percent of these provinces, i.e., in 18 out of 28 provinces, in
which these discrepancies (plus or minus) were
over 1 million decares, farms with over 500 decares were reported in the sample. But the proportion of provinces in which large farms were
located in the sample to all provinces surveyed
was only 38 percent (twenty-three provinces with
large farms out of the total of sixty-one provinces surveyed). This suggests that the di-
vergences in the land areas are due to an ap-
preciable degree to the number of large farms in
these provinces included in the sample, i.e., too
many in some and too few in others.[9] Of course,
these errors would to a large extent cancel out
if the plus and minus discrepancies were evenly
distributed among high and low income provinces.
But they are not. On balance among the twenty-
eight provinces the overstatements (plus) in the
sample are smaller in the areas where the average
crop and animal incomes are high, and the understatements (minus) are smaller in the areas where
these incomes are low.[10] Therefore one is led
to suspect that relatively too few large farms
are reported in the high income areas and relatively too many in the low income areas and
that, as a consequence, the average income per
decare of large farms in the sample is smaller
than it should be.

There is evidence to support this suspicion. Thus it is possible to compare the location of the number of farms with over 500 decares
in the sample with that of the number of large
independent farms[11] and of the number of farms
with over 1,000 decares.[12] These two latter
sets of statistics are derived from the 1950 census of agriculture and not based on a sample,
but on complete enumeration. This comparison
shows that, according to the data based on census enumeration, 85-87 percent of all large farms
(either independent or with over 1,000 decares)
were located in regions with gross crop and animal incomes per decare above the national av-

erage, while according to the sample of the distribution of land operated 68 percent of all farms with over 500 decares were located in areas with a higher average crop and animal income than the national average.

The comparison, of course, hinges on the assumption that there is a relationship between the regional location of the number of farms with over 500 decares and the location of farms with over 1,000 decares or of independent farms. But if this assumption is correct, it would follow that large farms are located in provinces with better than average crop and animal incomes per decare to a larger extent than the large farms reported in the distribution of land operated. It should also be noted that this comparison only involves the number of large farms and not their areas, when it is the area of large farms in high and low income provinces that determines their average gross income per decare. It is highly likely, however, that the same result would be attained if areas could have been compared.

From what has been said so far one would expect that the arithmetic mean income of the distribution of gross crop and animal incomes would be smaller than it should be since large farms in high income areas are understated, thereby tending to pull the mean down. But when the mean of this distribution is compared with one computed from non-sample data of totals (total income divided by total number of farms)[13] it actually turns out to be greater. The reason for this must be sought in the location of the medium size farms. Their number in provinces with high crop and animal incomes per decare is likely to be overstated and/or their number in low income areas understated,[14] and the cumulative effect of both factors apparently more than compensates, thereby pushing the mean upward. The effect of these factors on the inequality of crop and animal incomes computed from this sample distribution should be two-fold. The sampling error with respect to large farms tends to make the income distribution more equal than it should be and the sampling error with respect to medium size farms would tend in the other direction. While the two cannot be said to balance out precisely, whatever bias is introduced because of these two factors is probably not great. It should be added that since this whole question primarily concerns farms above the average size, the median crop and animal income per farm is not likely to be affected by these considerations since the positional sequence in the area of the median is probably not changed.

In the case of crop incomes alone, the picture is similar. If the mean gross crop income per farm is computed directly from the non-sample data, it comes out lower than in the distribution of gross crop incomes computed from Chapter VI, Table 2 (see page 85),[15] indicating that, on the whole, the number of farms in high crop income areas is overstated and in low income areas understated. But again for the large farms the reverse seems to be the case. 65 percent of all large farms in the sample were included in areas with crop incomes per decare above the national average, while according to the data based on census enumeration--the independent large farms and farms with over 1000 decares[16]--81-84 percent of the large farms are located in these better regions. Since the mean income in the distribution is too high, but the income of large farmers is rather too low, it seems that here too, it is the income of the medium-size farms that is too high, i.e., that too many medium-size farms are included in high income areas and that this more than compensates for the fact that too many large farms are included in low income provinces. Thus, in this instance, too, it is likely (1) that the median crop income is little affected by the sampling error and (2) that income inequality for the over-all distribution is neither over- nor under stated to any significant degree.

APPENDIX F

NOTE ON THE POSSIBLE USE OF 1963
CENSUS OF AGRICULTURE DATA

There were two instances in the text where data
from the 1963 Census of Agriculture,[1] which became available when this study was being revised,
could have been used but were not. The two estimates are the distribution of paid rent and
the distribution of animal incomes. These instances are considered in this appendix.

I. Recomputation of the Distribution of
     Paid Rent and Effect on the
     Distribution of Net Crop Income

         The distribution of paid rent (in Chap-
ter VII), although based on statistics referring
to the early 1950's, i.e., to the same period to
which the estimates in this book pertain, had
been derived very indirectly--partly on the
basis of assumptions that are reasonable but
could not be verified--since national data on the
distribution of land rent or area rented were
not available. The new census on the other hand
contains data from which a distribution of paid
rent can be derived more directly. The question
therefore arose as to whether the new data could
be used to derive better estimates. The answer
depends both on whether there have been significant changes in the distribution of paid rent
between the early 1950's and 1963 and on the
quality of the new data. Unfortunately, the
available data bearing on both these points are
very limited. A comparison of the 1950 and 1963
censuses of agriculture shows that the percentage
of all farm families who are tenants (both full
tenants who rent all the land they operate, and
part tenants who own some or most of their farms

and rent the rest), increased from 26 percent to 30 percent of all farm families.[2] This change is not very large, but while it has some bearing on changes in total rent payments, it certainly does not preclude the possibility that the distribution of rent paid could have become more or less equal.[3] So far as the quality of the rent data is concerned, all that can be said is that a comparison of the 1950 with the 1963 data shows about the same proportionate increase for full as for part tenants[4] and that such a result seems more reasonable than an erratic pattern under conditions where the overall changes have not been very great. But this evidence is not very strong.

In spite of the questions concerning the usability of the 1963 data for the above estimates, for trial purposes, the distribution of net crop incomes was recomputed with the new data, i.e., the distribution of land rented in the 1963 census was used to estimate the portion of crop costs of each land bracket that is attributable to land rent. The recomputed distribution came out more unequal than the original one (in Table 3 of Chapter VII), but the difference between the two was not very large. The shares of total income earned by the seven lowest tenths of all families remains practically unchanged, those of the second and third highest tenths become about three-fourths of 1 percentage point smaller, and the share of the highest tenth comes out to be 2.4 percentage points larger.[5]

In the text the distribution based on the data for rent paid for the 1950's was used[6] in spite of their shortcomings because it seemed better to do so in the absence of knowledge about the quality of the 1963 figures and particularly, in the absence of any very good basis for gauging the extent to which the distribution of rent paid may have changed between 1950 and 1963.

II. The Distribution of Animal Incomes

The 1963 census data could also be used
to compute a distribution of animal incomes,
since the census contains statistics on the distribution, by land brackets, of the number of
each type of livestock in Turkey, and these are,
of course, directly pertinent for such an estimate. Here, too, whether use of these data
would improve the estimates made in the text depends both on the extent to which there had been
changes between 1950 and 1963, and on the quality
of the 1963 data. No specific information on
changes is available, but in light of the fact
that between the two dates there was extensive
plowing up of pasture land, it may well be that
significant changes in the distribution of animal incomes did take place. With regard to the
quality of the data, a rough test of the over-
all magnitudes suggests that the data are usable.
The test consists of a comparison of the total
numbers of each kind of non-work animal in the
census with the corresponding numbers in the official statistics published yearly by the State
Institute of Statistics (previously the Central
Statistical Office). The comparison does not
take account of age differences in animals since
the yearly data do not give such breakdowns.
The numbers in the census turn out to be consistently lower, the differences ranging from
5 percent to 15 percent. However, since the
census excludes perhaps 10 percent of all farmers in the nation, as it does not cover most
farms located in places with more than 5,000
population, this difference appears reasonable.[7]
Though general knowledge suggests that
because of the reduction in pasture land changes
between 1950 and 1963 make it treacherous to use
the 1963 data for present purposes, a trial distribution was calculated on the basis of these
data. Such a distribution could be derived from
the census by assuming that the value of the number of livestock is an indication of the value

of the amount of animal products they produce.
The proportions in the census (pp. 61-64) of
each type of livestock, regardless of age, owned
by farm families in each land bracket, were rearranged by decile groups, and the results weighted by the average value of each of these animals
in 1950-1951. (See Appendix C, pp. 203-4.)
The result should be a distribution of animal incomes in which the distribution among land brackets is taken from the 1963 census, but the
relative importance of the products produced by
each type of animal applies to the early 1950's.

An examination of the new distribution
reinforces the initial feeling that these data
should not be used. It was seen in Chapter VIII
that implausible results were derived when combining the distributions of crop and animal incomes;[8] this could have been due either to the
fact that the distribution of animal incomes used
was more equal than it should have been, or that
the relative weight for animal incomes used in
combining the two distributions (which was derived from the official data), was too large, or
to a combination of both. There was no really
satisfactory way of resolving this problem because no good basis existed for deriving either
more adequate weights or a new distribution in
which one would have more confidence. Since it
was quite clear that, for one reason or the
other, the distribution of crop and animal incomes first calculated in Table 5 of Chapter VIII
gave too much weight to animal incomes and was
therefore too equal, it was averaged with a distribution of crop and animal incomes that was
too unequal (derived by assuming that the animal portion of these incomes was distributed in
proportion to size of farm land operated) to obtain a more balanced, if not perfect, final distribution.[9] But the distribution of animal incomes computed from the 1963 data is even more
equal than the one originally derived in Chapter VIII which was too equal.[10] To use these

figures, therefore, would only aggravate the problem. For this reason, as well as the others noted in the text, they were not used.[11]

NOTES AND BIBLIOGRAPHY

CHAPTER I

INTRODUCTION

[1] This is a rough, but fairly good approximation. Turkey is divided into 9 regions, of which regions I, IX, VIII, V, and VI (North Central, South Central, East Central, North East, South East) correspond fairly closely to the interior plateau, and regions II, III, IV, and VIII (Aegean, Marmara, Mediterranean, Black Sea) to the coastal areas and European Thrace. The proportions of the total crop area above are those included in the interior and coastal regions. (Source: Turkey, Prime Ministry, Central Statistical Office, Agricultural Structure and Production, 1946-54 [Publication No. 363; Ankara: Central Statistical Office, 1955], pp. 3-4. Data refer to 1953-54.)

[2] An exception has to be made for the Aegean region (region II), one of Turkey's richest areas. The eastern part of this region already comprises the edges of the central plateau, and in some drought years the whole region becomes an extension of Anatolia's dry interior.

[3] Cereals account for 75% of the country's total crop area, wheat alone for 44% and barley for 17%. (From ibid., pp. 3 and 8. Data refer to 1953-54.)

[4] Cereals accounted for 84% of the crop area in the interior (regions I, V, VI, VIII, IX) and for 59% in the coastal areas (regions II, III, IV, VII). From Turkey, Prime Ministry, Central Statistical Office, Agricultural Structure and Production, 1946-53 (Publication No. 351; Ankara:

Central Statistical Office, 1954), pp. 3-4 and 14-30. (Data refer to 1951-52.)

[5]George E. Brandow, "Agricultural Development in Turkey" (U.S. Foreign Operations Administration, Ankara, 1953 [mimeographed]), pp. 18-19.

[6]Food and Agricultural Organization of the United Nations, Turkey, Country Report, FAO Mediterranean Development Project (Rome: Food and Agricultural Organization of the United Nations, 1959), Chapter II, map following p. 2.

[7]Ibid., Chapter III, p. 15.

[8]Quentin M. West in Agricultural Development in Turkey, Effects on Products Competitive with U.S. Farm Exports, Foreign Agricultural Service, Foreign Agriculture Report No. 106, U.S. Department of Agriculture (Washington: U.S. Government Printing Office, January 1958), p. 24, states that peasants typically keep on hand one or two years supply of wheat. But the estimates shown in, Turkey, Prime Ministry, Central Statistical Office, Monthly Bulletin of Statistics, No. 64, pp. 148-150, indicate that these stocks are much smaller. The latter estimate is not based on any statistical survey, and the former does not appear to be either.

[9]For example, Mahmut Makal describes the hardships caused by the drought of 1949 in Village in Anatolia (London: Vallentine, Mitchell and Co., 1954).

[10]2,960,000 households and 5.71 members per household in 1955. (Turkey, Prime Ministry, Central Statistical Office, 1955 Population Census of Turkey [Publication No. 372; Ankara: Central Statistical Office, 1957], p. 52.)

[11]Turkey, Prime Ministry, Central Statistical

Office, 1950 Census of Agriculture (Statistical
Résumé No. 12/s: 1; Ankara: Central Statistical
Office, 1953), p. 13.

[12]Ibid., p. 8.

[13]Turkey, Prime Ministry, Central Statistical
Office, 1950 Agricultural Census Results (Publi-
cation No. 371; Ankara: Central Statistical
Office, 1956), p. 2.

[14]About 11% of all rural families. (For the
number of landless workers see Chapter II,
page 24 and for the number of rural farm fam-
ilies--excluding the landless workers--see ibid.,
p. 124.) The remaining rural population is
either engaged in non-agricultural pursuits
such as work in local flour mills, coffee houses,
blacksmith shops and the like, and a very small
proportion practice livestock raising exclusively.
The greater part of these are probably nomads,
who are still found in the eastern parts of the
country. (See Turkey, Prime Ministry, Central
Statistical Office, 1949 Village Census Summary
Results [Publication No. 344; Ankara: Central
Statistical Office, 1953], p. 12, for occupa-
tions of non-agricultural rural population, and
for the number of livestock families, 1950 Census of Agriculture, p. 7.)

[15]Calculated from ibid., p. 11.

[16]This is the average ratio in the country. The
ratio varies in different parts of the country
and is lower in the coastal areas. (See Agricultural Structure and Production, 1946-54,
pp. 3-4.)

[17]John A. Morrison, Alişar: A Unit of Land Oc-
cupance in the Kanak Su Basin of Central Anatolia (Chicago: University of Chicago Libraries,
1939), pp. 32 and 35-36.

[18]Brandow, op. cit., p. 25.

[19]Monthly Bulletin of Statistics No. 34-36, p. 169.

[20]Ibid., p. 169.

[21]Faculty of Political Science, University of Ankara, Türkiye'de Zirai Makinalaşma (Ankara 1954), Table 100 shows that only about 0.5% of all tractors were owned cooperatively, and 0.3% by villages. (This book is the Turkish edition of Faculty of Political Science, University of Ankara, Economic and Social Aspects of Farm Mechanization in Turkey [Ankara, 1953]. The reason for using the tables in the Turkish rather than the English edition is explained below in note 33.)

[22]Türkiye'de Zirai Makinalaşma, Tables 88 and 89 compared.

[23]Ibid., Tables 88, 89, 92, 93.

[24]Calculated from 1950 Agricultural Census Results, pp. 2-3.

[25]According to the official estimates animals and animal products constitute on the average about 1/3 of the gross farm income, and crop products 2/3. But there is reason to believe that the importance of animal products is overestimated. See Appendix C above.

[26]As will be seen in what follows, the data found most useful for this study (contained in what will be referred to as the Village Study) are unpublished. It was only by coincidence that the writer heard about it and was able to acquire this material. The source was first mentioned by Piraye Bigat, Research Director of the Agricultural Bank of Turkey at the time (spring of

1957) when the conversation took place. Miss
Bigat, who had been one of the field directors
for the study, did not have a copy of the report and had never seen the results. Neither
had anyone else in the field whom the writer was
able to contact. Repeated inquiries seemed to
lead nowhere until Nafiz Erus, at the time Head
of the Agricultural Division at the Central Statistical Office, suggested that the writer in-
quire at the Bureau of Agricultural Economics
of the Ministry of Agriculture. It was from
this source that the report was acquired. The
writer was most surprised to find that it was
available since she had been told previously by
a number of individuals in the field of agricultural economics, including a government official,
that they had attempted to find the report but
had not succeeded. So far as the writer is aware,
the copy of the study used by her is the only one
that has ever left the offices of the Bureau of
Agricultural Economics.

27Two examples might be cited. (1) In Monthly
Bulletin of Statistics No. 29, p. 125, one reads
that in 1954 wage earners constituted 14.84% of
those who paid income taxes. There is no mention
of the fact that the bulk of workers though they
pay income tax, are not included in these figures. Workers have their tax withheld and are
not required to file returns at the end of the
year. The published figures include only those
who filed returns because they earned at least
some income from which no taxes had been withheld. Excluded from the published figures, too,
and for the same reasons, are government employees, all of whom pay income tax. (2) In Monthly
Bulletin of Statistics No. 23, p. LXIII, establishments are listed in accord with the number
of workers employed. The total number of workers of all establishments in each class is reported. By dividing the total number of workers
in any class by the number of establishments in
that class, the resultant average should fall

within the limits of that class. But not all of
them do. The reason is that in setting up the
classifications, <u>unpaid family</u> workers were included as workers, but in listing the total number of workers in each class only <u>paid</u> workers
were included. In neither of the cases noted
was any warning or explanation given which would
put the reader on guard. These instances, as
well as many others, were found by checking the
data for plausibility and for internal consistency.

In the field of agricultural statistics
no such obvious instances of misleading headings
have been found, but there are ambiguities which
will be noted where the data are used.

[28]The term "test of consilience" is used by
A.F. Burns and W.C. Mitchell, <u>Measuring Business Cycles</u> (New York: National Bureau of Economic Research, 1946), pp. 506-508.

[29]It was undertaken by the Central Statistical
Office as a second phase of the 1950 agricultural census and is published with the other
census findings in <u>1950 Agricultural Census Re-
sults</u>.

[30]This study was undertaken by the Economics
Section of the Ministry of Agriculture of Tur-
key, with the assistance of the Agricultural
Division of the Central Statistical Office of
Turkey and of the Foreign Operations Administra-
tion. Vincent Lindquist, U.S. expert at the
Central Statistical Office, designed the sample.

[31]The villages were chosen in the areas located
between the provinces of Eskişehir and Sivas, and
Çorum and the Taurus mountains. This roughly
corresponds to the administrative regions I

(North Central) and XI (South Central), although
some of the western provinces of region I seem
to be excluded and some provinces belonging to
region VIII included.

32This information was given to me by George
Brandow of the Foreign Operations Administration of the U.S. and by Reşat Aktan, at the time
doçent in the Faculty of Economics at the University of Ankara, and one of the field directors of the survey.

33In the Turkish version of the study which was
published somewhat later, some corrections were
made in the tables that had been overlooked in
the English version. As a result, all statistics
that are used in this book are taken from the
Turkish version: Türkiye'de Zirai Makinalaşma.
(The table numbers in the Turkish and English
versions do not correspond.)

34Monthly Bulletin of Statistics No. 19, p.31.

35The region is not a governmental unit of administration as is the province.

PART I

FUNCTIONAL DISTRIBUTION
OF INCOME: Introduction

[1]There are some exceptions to this. There
exists some privately owned pasture land in regions where the large estates cannot secure the
necessary labor to use the land for crops. In
addition, there are instances where landlords
own whole villages, which may include pasture
land. In this case the landlord would get rent
for the use of the pasture land as well as the
crop land. Such a situation is described by
Edward Frederick Nickoley, in "Agriculture,"
Modern Turkey, ed. Eliot Grinnell Mears (New York:
Macmillan, 1924), p. 295. In addition fallow
land is used for pasture, but even though fallow
land, like all land used for crops, is owned
privately, when used as pasture land it is not
restricted to the animals owned only by the
owner of the fallow land. (John A. Morrison,
op. cit., p. 52.)

[2]See, however, pp. 64-69 above.

[3]Because of questions that arise about the official figure for the total crop product for
1951, the estimates derived in this chapter
which are based on the official figure are considered preliminary. Adjustment for this factor is made in Chapter IV.

CHAPTER II

FUNCTIONAL DISTRIBUTION OF CROP INCOMES
ACCORDING TO THE MARKET SYSTEM

[1]See, for example, David Ricardo, The Principles
of Political Economy and Taxation (New York:
E. P. Dutton, 1943, reprint of the third edition),
p. 1.

[2]See, for example, Frank H. Knight, Risk, Uncertainty and Profit (New York: Houghton Mifflin
Co., 1921).

[3]This is the conception developed by Frank
Knight in ibid.

[4]As pointed out above, no adjustment will be
made in this total at this stage to allow for a
greater or smaller crop output in 1951 than during a "normal year." This question will, however, be treated in Chapter IV when the results of the distribution of crop incomes according to the market and the shares system
will be compared.

[5]The gross crop product (of TL. 4,369 million),
less non-factor crop costs other than those ascribed to work animals, and net of depreciation
and indirect taxes, amounted to TL. 3,570 million
in 1951, according to Turkey, Prime Ministry,
Central Statistical Office, Türkiye Millî Geliri,
1938, 1948-51 (Publication No. 352; Ankara:
Central Statistical Office, 1954), p. 17,
Table 5.

[6]In Appendix C, page 207, the costs of work animals are estimated to have amounted to TL. 313
million in 1951.

[7]TL. 3,257 million as a percent of the value of
TL. 4,369 million given in note 5 above.

[8]There is reason to believe, as will be shown in Chapter IV, that this estimate is too high. Attempts to adjust for this overestimate are made in Chapter IV.

[9]In 1950 the number of permanent agricultural workers was 315,000 (1950 Agricultural Census Results, p. 2), and the total number of village families 2,760,000 (ibid., p. 2).

[10]As compared with the permanent agricultural workers of 315,000 in 1950 (see preceding note) there were 559,000 persons who left the villages temporarily in search of wages (ibid., p. 2.) The number in 1949 was 547,000. (1949 Village Census, p. 10.)

[11]For details, see pp. 150-51 above.

[12]Calculated from ibid., p. 10, which shows that 449,000 workers left their villages in search of work in villages other than their own and spent 20,700,000 man-days in these villages, giving an average of 46 days per worker spent in other villages.

[13]1950 Agricultural Census Results, p. 2, gives the number of permanent agricultural workers in cities and villages as 314,824. (For administrative purposes Turkey is divided into some 60 provinces and each province in turn into sub-areas called "kazas." Only the district seat of the "kaza" is called a "city," all other settlements are "villages," and the agricultural statistics are classified along these administrative lines. Since cities and villages are not distinguished by size of population, some "cities" are very small and rural, and some "villages" relatively large urban centers. For this reason agricultural workers are also found in "cities.") The 1955 Population Census of Turkey, p. 47, lists 309,229 persons employed in agriculture.

14The increase in the agricultural population between 1950 and 1951 was 2%. (Calculated from ibid., p. 10, on the assumption that population increase took place in geometric progression.)

15The 1955 Population Census of Turkey gives employment data for persons 15 years and over, but the 1950 Agricultural Census Results does not specify a lower age limit for the number of permanent agricultural workers. However, in the questionnaire upon which the data in the 1950 Agricultural Census Results are based (shown in ibid. p. 155) the pertinent question refers to the number of permanent (year round) agricultural workers hired by households or villages, and it is unlikely that there are many children hired on a year round basis. Nevertheless, the decrease in the number of permanent agricultural workers between 1950 and 1955 in the statistics may in part be due to the inclusion of a wider age group in 1950.

16The number of workers here includes the shepherds who tend non-work animals. As the income derived from non-work animals does not constitute a part of the crop product, the inclusion of these workers overstates the number of workers who are earning crop incomes. The error, however, should be small, and is probably more than compensated for by the understatement in the amount of seasonal work done for pay noted on page 25 above.

17Reported by Richard D. Robinson, "Village Economics," p. 3. Letter No. 36 of Letters on Turkey for the Institute of Current World Affairs and American University Field Service, New York, August, 1949.

18The total of TL. 744, which served as the point of departure in making this estimate, can be broken down as follows. Cash equivalent paid

in grain, TL. 574.51 (this is the minimum paid
if the yield is poor, although during better
crop years this item is paid as a share of the
crop); equivalent in food, TL. 142.51; soap,
TL. 2; clothing, TL. 40; housing, TL. 15. To
apply these figures to 1951 they were adjusted
to allow for a slight increase in the prices of
food and clothing and a decrease of the price of
soap between 1948 and 1951. Housing was not adjusted on the assumption that it is unaffected
by such minute price changes, and neither was
the cash equivalent in grain since government
purchase prices for grain had not changed between 1948 and 1951. (The adjustment for price
changes was made for food by using the average
for all regions of the regional index of food
prices shown in Turkey, Ministry of Commerce,
Konjonktür, January-March 1958, p. 25, and the
clothing allowance was increased by using the
average index of the price of clothing in the
Ankara cost of living index [shown in ibid.,
p. 19].)

[19]Average yearly wages are shown to be TL. 707
(Village Study, Table 23), including wages paid
in kind plus the estimated value of food provided. The income in kind not included in this
figure is clothing and housing. The value of
these items was added on the basis of the breakdown given by the Director of Gaziantep Province.
But since the Village Study data refer to 1953,
those for Gaziantep to 1948, and the wage figure needed for these estimates should refer to
1951, price adjustments had to be made for some
wages paid in kind. The sources used for these
adjustments are the same as those mentioned in
the previous note.

[20]See note 12 to this chapter for details on
these data. The number of man-days worked can
be checked indirectly. On the same page as the
number of man-days, the 1949 Village Census also
lists 547,000 workers leaving villages to seek

work outside (and the difference between this number and the 499,000 workers coming to villages should consist of villagers who went to work in cities). In the 1950 Agricultural Census Results, p. 2, the number of "outside going (sic) workers for wages" is 549,492, i.e., almost the same as the corresponding figure of 547,000 in the 1949 Village Census.

[21]Data on the size of the rural population in 1950 and 1955 are given in the 1955 Population Census (see preceding note), and for 1945 in, Turkey, Prime Ministry, Central Statistical Office, Annuaire Statistique 1953 (Publication No. 360, Vol. 21; Ankara: Central Statistical Office), p. 44. The 1949 and 1951 figures are interpolated on the assumption that the population increased in geometric progression.

[22]Mechanization Study, Table 116.

[23]Village Study, Table 23.

[24]TL. 64 on a monthly basis, derived from the Village Study yearly wage, including the estimated value of housing and clothing.

[25]Reşat Aktan, a leading Turkish agricultural economist, estimates that harvest wages would be somewhat more than twice as high as yearly wages if calculated for the same period.

[26]The number of males in agriculture (calculated as 3,159,000) is interpolated from data given for males 15-19 years of age and 15-64 years in the 1955 Population Census, p. 22 and then adjusted for the change in the size of the agricultural population between 1951 and 1955. For the source of the rural population data see note 14 to this chapter.

[27]Mentioned by Wilhelm von Flügge, "Untersuchungen und Materialien zur türkischen Volkswirtschaft," in "Sonderbericht zum deutsch-türkischen
Handelsverkehr" (Istanbul University, 1936.
Mimeographed.)

[28]Paul Stirling, Turkish Village (London:
Weidenfeld and Nicolson, 1965), p. 47.

[29]"Mémorandum présenté par l'expert turque."
Report submitted to Economic Commission for
Europe. (Mineographed.) The report is undated;
it was written sometime during the second half
of the 1950's.

[30]Compare the estimate of imputed wages assuming that the value of labor is equal to the
yearly wage of permanent agricultural workers,
and the estimate of wages according to the
marginal product of labor on pp. 29-30, sections
C (1) and C (2).

[31]See Eva Hirsch and Abraham Hirsch, "Changes in
Agricultural Output per Capita of Rural Population in Turkey, 1927-1960," Economic Development and Cultural Change, Vol. XI, (July 1963),
pp. 379-380.

[32]Paul Stirling, op. cit.

[33]John A. Morrison, op. cit., p. 54.

[34]This was mentioned to the author by the Director of the Istanbul Employment Office. His observation referred to the year 1958, when this
interview took place, but could almost certainly
be generalized to other years as well.

[35]From the 1955 Census of Population, p. 47.
The 1955 figures were adjusted to allow for the
fact that the agricultural population was smaller
in 1951. This was done by reducing the 1955
figures by the percentage difference between the

size of the rural population in 1951 and 1955. This difference was interpolated from the data for 1950 and 1955 shown in ibid., p. 10.

The figure for males may be somewhat too low as the difference between the number of males and females points to the temporary migration of males to towns in search of work, and a number of these return for a short period to help with the harvest.

36Von Flügge, op. cit., mentions that F. J. G. Christiansen-Weniger figures women's harvest work to be equivalent to 2/3 of men's work.

37This is the period for cereals, the main crop in Turkey. According to information supplied by Reşat Aktan, at the time doçent at the University of Ankara, and Nafiz Erus, former Director of Agricultural Statistics, Central Statistical Office, Ankara.

38This figure includes the harvest wages calculated earlier since temporary agricultural workers mostly do harvest work for others in addition to helping with their own harvest, and therefore should be counted twice.

39A rate of 56% may appear surprisingly high. It should, however, be borne in mind that tractors helped to overcome one of the very serious shortages in Turkish agriculture, the shortage of draft power during the plowing seasons, and that for that reason the crop yield from mechanized agriculture is considerably higher than from unmechanized agriculture. In a semi-arid climate mechanized operations increase yields per hectare both because they make possible more timely operations and better care of fallow land. Thus George Brandow, op. cit., p. 25, reports that 12 years of experiments at the Ankara Research Institute showed that the yield of small grains declined drastically when seeding took place after October (to 62% of the October yield

when seeding was done in November, and to still
lower proportions when seeding was done in later
months), and when the fall rains come late the peasants may not be able to get the seeding done by
October. Moreover, if the plowing season is
short, peasants have no time to plow the fallow
land in addition to plowing and seeding the
crop land, and Brandow reports (op. cit., pp. 25
and 27) that fallowing without follow-up cultivation produces yields that are about 40% lower
than when there is follow-up cultivation. For
these reasons a high rate of return on investment in tractors does not appear unreasonable.

Moreover, a rate of 56% does not seem to be
unusually high for the country generally. Thus
the United Nations, Department of Economic and
Social Affairs, in The Development of Manufacturing Industry in Egypt, Israel and Turkey (New
York: United Nations, 1958), p. 51, shows that
the anticipated rate of return (before taxes)
of private projects financed by the Industrial
Development Bank of Turkey in the years 1951 to 1953
varied between 21 and 78%. Even though taxes
would reduce these figures somewhat, a rate of
56% does not seem to be out of line with rates
of return that can be earned in fields outside
of agriculture.

[40]Mechanization Study, Table 111.

[41]This number was 24,000 according to the Monthly
Bulletin of Statistics, No. 34-36, p. 169.

[42]Calculated from Mechanization Study, Tables
111 and 24. The new value per tractor was
TL. 8,897, and the new value of other equipment
per tractor TL. 3,031.

[43]The number of tractors of different ages exis-
ting in Turkey in 1957 is shown in the Monthly
Bulletin of Statistics, No. 42-43, p. 157, and
from this one can calculate the age of tractors
in 1951. By assigning to these tractors the

average new value of the tractors in the Mechanization Study and by deducting a depreciation
rate of 12.5%, it was found that the average
value had to be reduced 13.5% for depreciation.
The depreciation rate of 12.5% was used because
according to the head of the agricultural section of the Central Statistical Office when this
estimate was made, the average life of a tractor
was 8 years. This 12.5% rate if somewhat smaller
than the rate of 15% used for motorized agricultural equipment in the national income calculations for Turkey. (Türkiye Millî Geliri, p. 16.)

[44]For the other equipment a rate of depreciation
of 10% was used since this is the rate applied
to equipment other than motors in the national
income calculations. (ibid., p. 17.) The average
total depreciation of this equipment was 10.8%;
this was derived in the same manner as that for
tractors in the preceding note, by assuming that
this equipment was of the same average age as
the tractors.

[45]The estimated value for tractors is TL. 185
million and for equipment TL. 65 million.

[46]1950 Agricultural Census Results, p. 4.

[47]Türkiye Millî Geliri, p. 19 and Appendix
Table 46.

[48]Turkey, Prime Ministry, Central Statistical
Office, Agriculture 1949-52 (Statistical Résumé
No. 9; Ankara: Central Statistical Office,
1953), p. 16, gives data on the number of work
animals in 1950 and 1951. The increase is 0.3%.

[49]Of this total TL. 946 million is the value of
work animals, and TL. 113 million the value of
the buildings. The latter is estimated in
Appendix C, p. 204.

[50]1950 Agricultural Census Results, p. 124, shows that the typical number of work animals owned is two, exclusive of donkeys. On page 4 of the same publication it is shown that the overwhelming number of work animals are oxen.

[51]See Appendix C for the derivation of this rate. Although theoretically imputed rent on common land would eventually become zero, it will be seen in Chapter V that it is likely that this process had not yet gone that far by 1951, which is why the rate of return derived in Appendix C includes some imputed rent. There is no way of estimating what proportion of this return should be considered rent. But even though the rate of 34% may be too high when taken as a rate of return on investment proper, the owners of work animals would earn the imputed rent just as the owners of non-work animals, since neither pays for the use of common land.

Theoretically, of course, rents and return on investments should not be grouped together. In this case, however, there is no way of separating them.

[52]TL. 750 million before, and TL. 637 million after depreciation. (From unpublished data supplied to the author.)

[53]On page 33 above this value was estimated at TL. 250 million net of depreciation.

[54]This figure is based on unpublished data representing details used to estimate the nation's national income, which have been supplied by the Central Statistical Office. It is calculated by subtracting from the estimated new value of all buildings used in agricultural production, first depreciation of TL. 25 million, and then the present value of buildings used for work animals of TL. 113 million, estimated earlier in this chapter.

[55]See text pp. 33-34 and note 51 to this chapter.

[56]Assuming that there are no "windfalls" or positive or negative profits.

[57]See pp. 20-21 above.

[58]It may appear that it would have been more logical to first adjust for the overestimate of crop income and then to derive the factor shares. This was not done because: (1) There is not complete agreement that the crop income used in this chapter was actually too large, so that it was felt necessary to derive the estimates shown in Table 1 of this chapter as well as those shown in Table 2 of Chapter IV. (2) Working with the revised figure would have much complicated the work of Chapter III. Those anxious to see the revised estimates and to examine how the revisions were made are advised to turn to Chapter IV, pp.55-60. The revised estimates are presented in the table on p.59.

CHAPTER III

FUNCTIONAL DISTRIBUTION OF CROP INCOMES
ACCORDING TO THE SHARE SYSTEM

[1]Evans Fotos, "Land Tenure and Rural Organization in Turkey Since 1923." Unpublished doctoral dissertation, American University, Washington, 1956.

[2]_Ibid._, p. 65.

[3]_Ibid._, p. 65.

[4]Richard D. Robinson, "Village Economics," _op. cit._ That seed may amount to half the total cost if expenses for wages, interest, and rent are deducted is shown in note 8 below.

[5]Richard D. Robinson, "Tractors in the Village," in _ibid._, February 15, 1952.

[6]Robinson mentions that still more common became a 1:3 system (and less frequently a 1:4 system) in which the owner provides the land, plows and seeds the fields (with tractors) and gets 2/3 (or 3/4) of the crop and the cropper bears the expenses of weeding the fields and picking the crop, and gets 1/3 (or 1/4) of the crop. (_Ibid._) For these systems one cannot readily gauge what rents would be since a part of the return to the landowner, who also owns the tractors, consists of a return on the investment in this equipment.

[7]For the predominance of cereals over other crops in the Village Study see Chapter VI, Table 9.

[8]The Village Study costs are shown in Table 2 of Appendix A. From this table one can calculate that for the farmers in the lowest land bracket seed costs are 50% of the total cost if expenditures for labor, interest and rent are omitted from the total costs. For the farmers in the

other land brackets seed costs are 55%, 47% and 42% of the total cost (going from the second-lowest to the highest land bracket) if wages, interest and rents are excluded from the total. The average is 50%. (To derive the average the percentages calculated for each land bracket above are weighted by the relative importance of farms of the size of those in the Village Study in the nation.)

[9] 14 tractors were owned by the 20 farmers in this land bracket, 4 by the 99 farmers in the next lower bracket, and none by the farmers in the two lowest land brackets. (From Village Study, Tables 1 and 19.)

[10] From Mechanization Study, Tables 88 and 89.

[11] E.g., Edward Frederick Nickoley, op. cit., p. 295, or Arthur Robert Burns, Comparative Economic Organization (New York: Prentice Hall, 1955), p. 79.

[12] See Table 4 in Chapter VI for a comparison of yields obtained with mechanized and unmechanized operations.

[13] Table 31 in the Village Study shows that only 50% of the farmers in the highest land bracket rent land.
It might seem inconsistent that some of the land of the farmers in the highest land bracket in the Village Study is not cultivated with trac-tors, and yet that these farmers seek to expand their operations because their tractors can cul-tivate more land. But this makes sense if one considers that not all the farmers in this land bracket own tractors, and that the land culti-vated without tractors is likely either to belong to unmechanized farmers or is devoted to crops that do not lend themselves to mechanized oper-ations such as tree crops.

[14]The rented land would probably be planted to wheat (since one finds on the basis of Tables 1, 3 and 6 in the Village Study that the largest farmers planted 72% of their non-fallow area to wheat), and in Central Anatolia the income of wheat land, if operated with tractors, is shown in the Mechanization Study to be 37% higher than for non-mechanized operations (see Chapter VI, Table 4). This would roughly give a yield of 140 kg. (Table 6 in the Village Study shows that wheat yields were 104 kg. per decare for the farmers in the lowest land bracket, and 100 kg., 108 kg., and 120 kg. for the farmers in the succeeding land brackets. But only the farmers in the two lowest land brackets owned no tractors at all, so that only their yields would represent the yields from totally un-mechanized operations. 140 kg. is then 137.5% of the average yield of farmers in the two low-est land brackets.) The Village Study (Table 10) shows further that the average price of wheat per kg. was TL. 0.28 for the farmers in the largest land bracket; with a yield of 140 kg. this gives a gross income per decare of TL. 39.20 from mechanized wheat cultivation. If one de-ducts from this twice the cost of seed per de-care of TL. 2.82 (calculated from Village Study, Tables 1 and 2 on the basis of the data for the largest land bracket), the net income per de-care, computed by considering costs to amount to twice the cost of seed, would be TL. 33.56. Rents of TL. 15 would then be a little less than 50% of this "net" product. But since the gross income of TL. 39.20 calculated from the Mechan-ization Study need not exactly apply to the mechanized operations in the Village Study, the actual ratio may even be closer to 50% than these calculations show.

[15]Village Study, Table 33.

[16]Rents of 50% of the gross output with seed costs borne by the landlord (as in Robinson's

example) are equal to rents of 50% of the "net" product if total costs are considered to consist of twice the cost of seed (which seems to be the share paid in the Village Study). For example, if the gross crop output is TL. 24 and the cost of seed TL. 3, rents of 50% of the gross output with seed costs to be borne by the landlord would give the landlord a rent of TL. 12 minus TL. 3, or TL. 9. And if the rent is calculated as 50% of the "net" output, it would be 50% of TL. 18 (TL. 24 minus twice TL. 3), or TL. 9 also.

[17]Robinson refers to cotton areas.

[18]Fotos refers to vineyard areas.

[19]Türkiye Millî Geliri, Appendix Table 61.

[20]Ibid., Appendix Table 6.

[21]From ibid., Appendix Tables 16 and 21.

[22]Calculated from Agricultural Structure and Production, 1946-54, p. 6, for 1952, by weighting the individual prices of fibre and seed by the relative output of seed and fibre shown on pp. 172-173 of the Monthly Bulletin of Statistics, No. 34-36. For earlier years, cotton prices were calculated from Türkiye Millî Geliri, Appendix Tables 16-18, which give the value of cotton output in current and in 1948 prices.

[23]Calculated from ibid., Appendix Tables 16 and 22.

[24]The reason why it is desirable, if anything, to understate rents will be apparent in the next chapter.

[25]Calculated from ibid., Appendix Tables 11, 21, and 61.

[26]The gross crop output of TL. 4,369 million and the national income originating in crop produc-

tion of TL. 3,257 million for 1951 are derived from the national income estimates. See p. 22 above.

[27]See note 16 to this chapter.

[28]Morrison, op. cit., p. 16. Morrison does not make it clear whether the proportion is 1/4 for wages alone, and 1/3 for wages plus the contribution of work animals, or whether the share of wages alone varies between 1/4 and 1/3. Since, as noted earlier, rents for cereal land account for 50% of either the gross or the net product, the ratios of 1/4 to 1/3 would be too small to refer to the share of both labor and capital combined and must, therefore, refer to wage incomes only.

[29]See p. 45 above.

[30]Morrison, op. cit., p. 16.

[31]See p. 22 above.

[32]Calculated from Appendix A, Table 2, p. 180.

[33]In the Village Study, non-factor crop costs, i.e., crop costs exclusive of expenditures that are factor incomes (rent, wages and interest), consist of: (1) seed, (2) depreciation and repair of equipment, (3) fuel and feed for work animals, (4) other costs of work animals (for animal shoes, saddles and harnesses, animal vaccination), (5) depreciation and repair of buildings for work animals and equipment, (6) cost of transport of crops to the market, of baskets, cord, sacks bought, of seed treatment and irrigation, and (7) fertilizer. (From Village Study, Tables 2 and 27.)
   Of these expenditures it was seen that the cost of seed (item 1) is borne either by the landlord or the peasant, depending on the type of crop grown. It seems safe to assume that

the cost of transportation of the crop to the
market, of baskets, cord, etc. (item 6) and of
fertilizer (item 7 above), is borne by the
tenant even if he does not supply the draft
power and tools. All remaining costs are costs
of capital in the sense that they involve costs
incurred for maintenance and operation of draft
power and tools and equipment (i.e., depreciation and repair of equipment, fuel for tractors
and feed for work animals, other costs of work
animals, depreciation and repair of buildings
for work animals and equipment [items 2, 3, 4,
and 5 above]).

34By converting the average expenditure for all
farms in the Village Study of each of the items
other than seed costs listed in the previous
note into percentages of total costs of 26%, a
figure of 1.8% was derived for costs ascribed
to labor (cost of transportation of the crop to
market, of baskets, cord, etc., bought, plus the
cost of fertilizer which is also likely to come
out of labor's share), and the remainder, 11%, to
capital (i.e., cost of equipment, fuel, feed of
work animals, cost of buildings for work animals,
and other costs of work animals). The data on
which these computations are based are shown in
Appendix A, Table 2.

35These calculations are shown in Table 3, lines
1-4. From the gross wage share (of 25-33%) are
deducted costs of 2%, from the share of capital
(of 25-17%) costs of 11%, and from the landlord's
share (of 50%) seed costs of 13%. The resulting
shares then add up to 74% since 26% of the
gross return has been deducted as costs. When
taken as a percent of the net product (i.e.,
74%), one obtains the figures in column 3 where
the shares are expressed as the net return of
the net product.

36From the gross labor share (of 25-33%) are deducted costs of 2% plus half the cost of seed, or

6½%. From capital's share (of 25-17%) are deducted costs of 11%, plus 6½% for half the seed. The resulting shares than add up to 74% since 26% of the gross return has been deducted as costs. When taken as a percent of the net product (i.e., 74%) one obtains the net shares of the net crop product shown in Table 3, column 3.

FUNCTIONAL DISTRIBUTION OF CROP INCOMES
ACCORDING TO THE MARKET SYSTEM
AND THE SHARE SYSTEM COMPARED

[1]Quentin M. West, op. cit., p. 33.

[2]See "Changes in Agricultural Output per Capita
of Rural Population in Turkey, 1927-1960,"
pp. 384-86.

[3]The reduction in the net crop product was made
as follows: First the gross crop output in constant 1948 prices was adjusted downward by reducing the cereal portion of this output 20% for
all years after 1950. Secondly, the normal value
for 1951 was computed by taking a 5-year average
of the adjusted data centered in 1951. (The
sources of the statistics on total crop output
as well as on the cereal portion of this output
is Türkiye Millî Geliri, Appendix Tables 5 to 8
for the years 1949 to 1951, and unpublished data
supplied by the Central Statistical Office for
1952 to 1954.) These two adjustments were applied to the gross crop output in 1951 at 1948
prices, and together resulted in a 10% reduction
in this output value. Therefore the gross crop
output in 1951 in current prices of TL. 4,369
million was reduced by the same proportion; from
the resulting adjusted gross figure the estimated
actual non-factor crop costs of TL. 1,112 million
was deducted, giving a value of TL. 2,828 million for the adjusted normalized national income
originating in crop production. (For the cost
data see notes 5 and 6 on p.245.

[4]No claims are made, of course, about the situation in other countries. So far as the writer
is aware no general studies have been done,
theoretical or empirical, comparing the conse-
quences of the two systems. Cursory examination

suggests that the fifty-fifty system is unusually popular generally.

CHAPTER V

FUNCTIONAL DISTRIBUTION OF CROP
AND ANIMAL INCOMES

[1]According to Stirling, op. cit., p. 57, in the village in Central Anatolia where he lived.

[2]See Ali Aran, Nevzat Gurpinar, and George Brandow, "A Survey of Grazing and Cattle Production in Erzurum Province" (U.S. Foreign Operations Administration, Ankara, 1953. Mimeographed). In this survey the season is reported to last 222 days. Riza Kazım in Die türkische Landwirtschaft und ihre wichtigsten Betriebszweige (Ankara, 1935), p. 127, reports that in the eastern provinces the winter season during which cattle cannot pasture outdoors lasts about 150 days, which gives about the same number of days or roughly eight months.

[3]Stirling, op. cit.

[4]Computed from Appendix A, Table 3. In calculating this proportion the net income was taken to be net only of costs that are not incomes of factors of production.

[5]The Village Study shows that most families use the services of paid shepherds (Table 22), and for those who do not the marginal product of their labor should be zero or very small during a substantial part of the work period. (See Chapter II, section III B, especially pp.26-29.

[6]Riza Kazım, op. cit., reports that any villager has the right to pasture as many animals on the village pastures as he owns. Kazım mentions only one reservation. A peasant who moves to another village does not thereby automatically acquire the right to graze his animals on the pastures of the new village. He must be granted this right by the inhabitants of the new village. (P. 122.)

Kazım's observation that villagers can, on
the whole, freely pasture as many animals as
they own corresponds to observations made by many
other persons familiar with Turkish agriculture.
However, Martin Hansmeier, in "Report and Recommendations Concerning Crops and Soils in Turkey" (Mutual Security Agency, Special Mission to
Turkey, November 1951. Mimeographed), states
that "There is some appreciation of the limited
capacity of pastures to carry stock, even though
the general level of stocking is excessive. Village committees exercise some control over the
number of stock to be held by each individual,
restricting the flock-size of each villager on
general grounds of equity, family needs and
village tradition." (P. 68.)

It was not possible for the writer to determine which of these two conflicting observations
corresponds to the more general situation, but
even Hansmeier's findings suggest that control
is not very extensive.

7Of course it is possible that the term "over-
grazing" refers to long-run destruction of pasture land rather than an absolute decline in the
net income from animals at the present. The
description quoted from Turkey, Country Report
in this paragraph in the text, however, leaves
little doubt as to which interpretation is the
correct one.

8Turkey, Country Report, op. cit., Chapter I,
p. 3.(Italics mine.) See also p. 214-15 above.

9Note in the table that the reduction in pasture
land is almost equal in area to the increase in
crop land. If area of field crops and fallow
alone had been compared to the area of pasture
land, the changes in the one would almost exactly
have offset the changes in the other.

10Harvey Oakes in "Final Report, Soil Survey and
Soil Management" (U.S. Foreign Operations Admin-

istration. T. A. Project 77-149, Ankara, May
1952 to May 1954) reports that a reconnaissance
survey on soils in Turkey indicated that only
16.4 million hectares of the total land area in
Turkey were suitable for cultivation. The data
in Table 1 show that in 1951 the total area under
crops was about 5% larger than this figure, but
that by 1960 it was over 50% larger.

[11]This is described by Morrison, op. cit., p. 40,
referring to the early 1930's and more recently
by Wilbur Harlan in "An Analysis of Wheat Production in Turkey" (I.C.A. Airgram: TOICA A-430,
November 16, 1956).

[12]Ultimately, however, the number of animals
would be restricted by the number that the pastures can support. This point, however, would
probably be way past the point of absolute diminishing returns when the average return on investments becomes so small that peasants do not find
it worth their while to add more animals to the
land.

[13]The formulas are described in Türkiye Millî
Geliri, pp. 17-19.

[14]If the net value of animals and animal products
is reduced by one-half, from TL. 1,771 million
to TL. 886 million, the over-all distribution of
crop and animal products according to the market
system in Table 4, p. 74, would change to 43% of the
total product going to wages, 39% to capital,
18% to land. Under the same conditions the distribution according to the share system in the
same table would become: 22-30% for wages,
30-37% for capital, 40% for land. Thus capital
would still get 39% of the total income in the
one distribution and 30-37% in the other.

PART II

DISTRIBUTION OF INCOME BY
INCOME SIZES: Introduction

[1]In the Turkish national income accounts interest earned on agricultural land is not counted as income originating in the agricultural sector but is included with income of the financial sector. Since wages earned in agriculture by urban residents are negligible, the only agricultural income accruing to city residents of consequence is rent.

CHAPTER VI

THE SHAPE OF THE DISTRIBUTION
OF GROSS CROP INCOMES

[1]The reliability of the statistics on the distribution of land operated is examined in detail in Appendix E.

[2]Thus, according to the data on the distribution of land operated, in the nation as a whole 62% of all farm families operated farms with less than 50 decares, while in the provinces of Rize and Trabzon along the Black Sea, the percentage is 95% and 98% respectively. The average value of crop output per decare in all of Turkey is TL. 28, but in Rize it is TL. 44, and in Trabzon TL. 69.

[3]The average gross crop income per decare for the 0-20 decare land bracket was TL. 35, and this average consistently declines until one reaches the 150-200 decare bracket where it is TL. 27. From this point on it consistently increases again, and reaches TL. 38 for the 700 and over land bracket. (In deriving these results the data on land operated were taken from the 1950 Agricultural Census Results, pp. 134-5, and the data on average income per decare were computed as explained in note a to Table 2.)

[4]The average gross crop incomes per decare was TL. 42 for the Mediterranean, TL. 40 for the Aegean, TL. 35 for the South East, TL. 33 for the Marmara, TL. 32 for the Black Sea and TL. 25 and under for the three Central Anatolian regions and the North East. (Computed as explained in note a to Table 2.)

[5]The figure on the percent of total agricultural income per province earned from industrial crops was derived from Türkiye Zirai İstihsal Kıymeti

1952, p. 4; those on the average gross income per decare earned from industrial crops and all crops from ibid., p. 4, and Agricultural Structure and Production, 1946-53, p. 12; data on percentage of fallow land to total crop land were derived from ibid., p. 3; and those on average gross income per decare earned from all crops from the sources cited in note a to Table 2.

[6]George Brandow, op. cit., p. 21.

[7]Monthly Bulletin of Statistics, No. 34-36 (all are in one issue), p. 169.

[8]Not considering fallow land, this figure came out to be 460 decares. It was derived as follows: The total area cultivated with tractors in the nation (except region V) was divided by the total number of tractors in the nation (except region V). Region V was omitted because the Mechanization Study contains no data on that region. However, the number of tractors in region V constituted only 1.5% of all tractors used in the nation, so that if this region had been included in the national total it would not significantly have affected the average. (For details of the estimated total area cultivated with tractors in the nation, see Appendix B, note 25.) With fallow land included, a tractor, on the average, cultivated 690 decares, since on the average one third of all cultivated land is fallow.

[9]Area cultivated by farms with over 500 decares from 1950 Census of Agriculture, Table 8.

[10]The average size mechanized farm in the Mechanization Study was 1,247 decares in Central Anatolia, 972 decares in the Mediterranean, 488 decares in the Aegean, 626 decares in the Marmara, 5,463 decares in Southeastern Anatolia, and 282 decares in the Black Sea region. Therefore, two regions, the Black Sea and the Aegean had av-

erage size farms of less than 500 decares. Together, however, these regions account for only
11% of the total area of mechanized farms in
1952. (Average farm sizes from Mechanization
Study, Table 88. Figure of 11% computed as
explained in note 25 to Appendix B.

[11]The extent to which the yields of large farmers
in the Village Study are higher than those of
small farmers could be explained by about 40%
mechanization, but roughly 50% of the area of
these farms is mechanized. Thus the yield of
large farmers without mechanization would be
smaller than that of the small farmers. This
result was estimated as follows: The large farmers in the Village Study operated a total of
19,142 decares and had 14 tractors. (Village
Study, Tables 2 and 19.) If each tractor operates 690 decares (the average calculated from
the Mechanization Study), the 14 tractors would
work 9,960 decares, which is 50.5% of the area
of the large farms in the Village Study. For
this degree of mechanization, their yields do
not seem to be high enough. Thus, over 80% of
the area of these large farms is planted to
wheat (Village Study, Table 3) so that these
tractors must be used for wheat land. According
to the Mechanization Study use of tractors in
Central Anatolia increases wheat yields by 37.5%
(computed from Table 4, pp. 91-92), but the wheat
yields of large farmers in the Village Study are
up only 15.4%, which could be explained by about
40% mechanization of wheat land (15% : 38%).
(Table 4 shows that tractors seem to have little
effect on barley yields, but only a small part
of the total area of large farms in the Village
Study is sown to barley and it may be that
little of this is cultivated with tractors.)

[12]For a more detailed discussion of this question
see Appendix D.

[13]Compare, for example, the differences between columns (1) and (2) in Table 4 with the differences in income per decare from industrial crops and from all crops, noted on p. 87.

[14]The figures on the degree of self-sufficiency in the Village Study are very rough. They show that the farmers in the lowest land bracket consumed 70% of their non-animal net income while those in the highest land bracket consumed 15%. (Computed from Village Study, Table 2.)   But according to G. E. Brandow who directed the study but had to leave before it was completed, the statistics on home-comsumed crops are likely to be the least reliable ones.

[15]Note the lower wheat yields of the small farmers in the Village Study in Table 6 on p. 95.

[16]This might appear to contradict what is shown in Table 7 for Central Anatolia, but this contradiction is only apparent.   In Table 7 it is shown that large farmers grow more cotton and beets, relative to wheat and barley, than small farmers.   But cotton and beets are the high-income crops which lend themselves especially well to mechanization.   So far as all high-income crops are concerned, it is likely that for all farmers in Central Anatolia the same relationship exists as for those of the Village Study.

CHAPTER VII

THE SHAPE OF THE DISTRIBUTION
OF NET CROP INCOMES

[1]Computed from Appendix A, Table 2 on p. 180.

[2]Compare in Table 2 on p. 113, lines 1 and 15.

[3]In the Village Study the full tenants are found in the lowest and the third lowest land brackets. The third lowest land bracket goes from 160 to 499 decares. It is likely that these families are not found at the upper end of this bracket.

[4]This proportion was derived by weighting the number of full renters in each land bracket in Village Study, Table 31, by the relative importance of the number of families in each of these land brackets in the nation. (See Appendix A, Table 1, note h.) If the full renters in the Village Study were weighted by the relative importance of the actual number of families included in each land bracket in the Village Study sample, their proportion would be 0.7%.

[5]Calculated from 1950 Agricultural Census Results, p. 122.

[6]The proportion of full tenants in the Village Study is 0.5%, while the proportion in regions I and IX combined, which roughly correspond to the regions included in the Village Study, is 1.3% in 1950 Agricultural Census Results.

[7]The proportion of full renters is 0.5% of all farm families in the Village Study, and 3.8% in the nation.

[8]The proportion of families who are part-renters to all farm families in the nation was calculated from 1950 Agricultural Census Results, p. 122,

and the corresponding proportion in the Village Study from Table 31 of that study.

[9]This is the weighted average of the seven-fold increase in the rents of full tenants and the 26% increase for part-tenants. The portion of all rents paid by full and by part-tenants in the lowest land bracket in the Village Study was derived from Table 31 of that study, on the assumption that part-tenants rent on the average half as much land as full tenants, and therefore pay half as much rent.

[10]For all farms in the nation the ratio was computed from 1950 Agricultural Census Results, p. 124, and from the 1953 data on the number of tractors (since the Village Study data refer to 1953) in Monthly Bulletin of Statistics, No. 64, p. 135. In computing this ratio it was assumed that all tractors in the nation were used on farms with over 500 decares. The Village Study ratio was computed from Tables 1 and 19 in the study.

[11]Computed from Village Study, Tables 28 and 31.

[12]Computed from Mechanization Study, Tables 88 and 89. The proportion of the area of land operated to the area of land owned, less 100%, gave the proportion of land operated that is rented.

[13]The average proportion of the land operated that is rented in the Mechanization Study was calculated separately for each region as explained in the preceding note. The average for all regions was computed as explained in Appendix B, note 25.

[14]Computed from Table 2 (p. 113).

[15]Computed from Table 2.

[16]Calculated from Village Study, Table 1, and Appendix A, Table 2, on p. 180 above.

[17]The estimated rate of return derived from investments in tractors and modern equipment is 56%. (See Appendix B, Table 1.)

[18]Large farmers irrigated 3% of their land, and small farmers 5%. (From Village Study, Table 4.)

[19]The large farmers planted 86% of their cultivated area to wheat and barley and the small farmers 79%. (Computed from Village Study, Tables 3, 6, and 8.)

[20]Wheat and barley are grown in every one of the 63 provinces of Turkey, and if one considers smaller geographic divisions than provinces, both crops are grown in 488 out of Turkey's 492 kazas (administrative subdivisions of provinces). This is shown in Türkiye Zirai İstihsal Kıymeti, 1952, pp. 6-15.

[21]The figures on home consumption in the Village Study are supposed to be the least reliable part of the study. But even if the figures are not precise, they are still indicative.

[22]See for example Eva Hirsch and Abraham Hirsch, "Changes in Agricultural Output per Capita of Rural Population in Turkey, 1927-1960," Figures 1 or 3.

[23]Compare the yield figures for 1951, 1952, and 1953 with those in preceding and following years in Monthly Bulletin of Statistics No. 34-36, p.170.

[24]Of course not all small farmers produce exclusively for subsistence. But insofar as they do, even if not exclusively, a larger proportion of their small plots would have to be devoted to satisfying the family needs than of the larger farms.

CHAPTER VIII

THE SHAPE OF THE DISTRIBUTION OF
NET CROP AND ANIMAL INCOMES

[1]Calculated from Türkiye Zirai İstihsal Kıymeti, 1952, p. 4. These data are for 1952. The proportion was roughly the same according to the national income estimates for 1948-51. (See Türkiye Millî Geliri, pp. 16 and 17. The figures in Türkiye Zirai İstihsal Kıymeti are based on the national income estimates.)

[2]The concept of "animal incomes per decare of (crop) land operated" does not imply, of course, that animal incomes were conceived of as being derived from crop land. Use of this concept rather served as a shorthand expression for the relation between size of animal income and size of land operated. For example, if it is said that animal incomes per decare of (crop) land operated are the same for two farms of different sizes, this means that the difference in the income from animals of the two farms is in exact proportion to the difference in the size of their farms.

[3]Data from the 1963 census of agriculture could have been used, but it is shown in Appendix F why this was not done.

[4]It is 22% higher, as the average gross crop income in the nation is TL. 28 (see note (a) to Table 4), and the average gross crop income in the Village Study is TL. 23 [derived by dividing the crop incomes shown in Appendix A (Table 2, line 1) for each land bracket, by the number of decares in that land bracket (shown in Village Study, Table 1), and by then averaging these per decare incomes according to the relative importance of farms in each of these land brackets.]

[5]Computed from Appendix A, Tables 2 and 3 above.

[6]For the farmers in the lowest land bracket consumption of home-produced animal products other
than wool (which should not be counted as food
consumption) amounted to 26% of all home-consumed crop and animal products (exclusive of
seed). The proportion of animal products consumed as food is somewhat smaller, 24%, since for
lack of sufficient detail in the Village Study
the computed ratio of 24% includes with consumption of animal products the value of whole animals
consumed on farms. (The pertinent data on home
consumption are shown in the Village Study,
Tables 2 and 15.)

[7]Shown in Konjonktür, January 1941, p. 13. The
study does not give separate data on consumption
of animal and vegetable fats. The proportion of
animal products and vegetable fats combined to
total food consumption ranged from 18% in the
Black Sea region to 26% in the Mediterranean.
For other regions surveyed it was 19% for Central
Anatolia, and 22% for both the Marmara and Aegean
regions. It should be added that this survey
was done during an unusually poor crop year and
is, therefore, not as representative as one
would like it to be.

[8]See Franz Eppenstein, "Die Ernährung des mittelanatolischen Bauern," in Revue de la Faculté des
Sciences Economiques, Université d'Istanbul,
Year I, 1940. (Eppenstein's data are based on
the same survey as the data published in Konjonktür.) The average proportion of animal products
as a percent of the value of food consumption in
Central Anatolia was 19%, as shown in the previous note, and applied to farms with incomes of
TL. 430. For farms with incomes of TL. 0-200
(the lowest income group shown) it was 21%.

[9]The gross crop and animal incomes of the small

farmers in the Village Study amounted to 62% of
the average of these incomes in the Village
Study, while that of the small farmers in the
Konjonktür survey for Central Anatolia was less
than half, and possibly much less, than the average income level for this region in the survey.
(For the incomes in the Konjonktür survey, see
the preceding note. The Village Study ratio is
computed from Appendix A, Table 1 above.)

[10]See p. 136-37 and note 6 to this chapter.

[11]The national ratio, which includes the eastern
regions, is 35%, and the ratio for all regions
in the nation except the eastern ones is 32%.
These ratios are computed from Türkiye Zirai
İstihsal Kıymeti 1952, p. 4, which are based on
the official estimates of the Central Statistical Office.

[12]They constitute 2.1% of all rural families
(1950 Census of Agriculture, Table 5).

[13]The final distribution in Table 6 is somewhat
more unequal than the estimate of the same distribution in my article "A Method of Estimating
the Distribution of Farm Incomes in Turkey,"
The Journal of Development Studies, Vol. II,
No. 2, January 1966, which essentially presents
a summary of the results of Chapters VI to VIII
above. However, the article includes separate
estimates of the distribution of crop and animal incomes; these were then combined by means
of a weighted average, where the weights were
based on revised estimates of the relative importance of each of these incomes in the official
data. In retrospect, however, this method of
deriving a combined distribution of crop and animal incomes appears to give less satisfactory
results than the method used above, which had
also been originally used in my dissertation,
i.e., that of deriving both an upper and lower
limit distribution, and then averaging the re-

sults. Although in this article the relative
importance of animal to crop incomes used for
weights to obtain the weighted average of the
two distributions was lower than that in the official data, in the weighted average distribution the small farmers would still derive nearly
half of their net crop and animal incomes from
animal products, a problem that I had not real-
ized at the time.

CHAPTER IX

THREE FINAL DISTRIBUTIONS OF INCOME FROM
AGRICULTURAL AND NON-AGRICULTURAL SOURCES
EARNED BY THE TURKISH FARM POPULATION

[1]Paid interest should not be deducted because in
the Turkish national income accounts earned interest does not constitute a part of the income
originating in agriculture, but is calculated as
part of the income of financial institutions.

[2]See p. 26.

[3]The proportion of privately operated land that
is rented, calculated from Turkey, Prime Ministry, State Institute of Statistics, 1963 Census
of Agriculture, Sample Survey Results (Publication No. 477; Ankara: State Institute of Statistics, 1965), pp. 6-7, is 15%. The average
portion of the crop paid as rent in share arrangements, which had been calculated on p. 47,
is 52%. The adjusted and normalized net crop
product in 1951 was estimated to have been
TL. 2,828 million. The estimated total rent
payments in 1951 were therefore 52% x 15% x TL
2,828 million, or TL. 229 million.

[4]Both proportions are 17% if the proportion of
families who are tenants is computed as explained
in note 5 below from ibid. pp. 2 and 6-7.

[5]If proportion of tenancy among farm families is
assumed to be an indication of proportion of
area of land that is rented, one must also assume
that farmers who own part of their farms and
rent the rest, rent on the average half as much
land as those who rent all the land they operate.
If both assumptions are made, one finds from the
data in the 1950 Census of Agriculture (p. 8) that
14 to 15% of all farm land is rented, and from
those of the 1963 Census of Agriculture (pp. 2, 3,

6, 7) that the corresponding proportion is 17%. Since rent, on the average, accounts for half of the net output of the land, the difference in rent payments would account for about one percent of this output.

It should be noted that in my dissertation, which was written before the 1963 census of agriculture was taken, I had estimated the total amount of rent payments by deriving the proportion of rented land from the data in the 1950 Census of Agriculture on the basis of the assumptions stated in paragraph 1 of this note. The result was almost the same as the proportion of the area rented by tenants derived directly from the 1963 census. However, I assigned to this land too much rent, in my present judgment, and this together with other revisions, accounts for the fact that the estimate of rent payments in my dissertation is larger than it is here.

[6]Derived as follows: (1) The official data of the national income originating in agriculture at constant 1948 prices were adjusted by reducing the income derived from cereals 20% for all years after 1950, and keeping the income from animal products constant after 1950. (For the reasons for this adjustment see Eva Hirsch and Abraham Hirsch, "Changes in Agriculture Output per Capita of Rural Population in Turkey, 1927-1960," especially pp. 381-86.) (2) From these adjusted data a least-squares trend was computed for the years 1948-58, and the adjusted and normalized 1951 value in 1948 prices was derived. (3) The value derived in (2) was then raised for the increase in agricultural prices between 1948 and 1951. For this purpose the implicit price index in the national income originating in agriculture in 1948 prices and in current prices was used. (Sources for national income originating in agriculture in current and 1948 prices: Monthly Bulletin of Statistics No. 55, pp. 118 and 122, and No. 80, pp. 132 and 136. Source of value of cereal output in 1948 prices: unpub-

lished data obtained from the Central Statistical Office.)

This figure differs from that used in deriving the estimates in Table 4 of Chapter V (on p. 74) because no adjustment is made here for the overestimate in animal output. This adjustment was necessary in Chapter V where the results were affected by the relative importance of crop and animal incomes. It is omitted here because no very satisfactory adjustment can be made for this overestimate, and because it would have little effect on the estimates in this chapter.

[7]Paul Stirling, _op. cit._

[8]Wilhelm von Flügge, _op. cit._

[9]_1963 Census of Agriculture_, p. 7.

[10]This proportion appears to be 73% and was calculated as follows: Of the total of 2,294,727 hectares rented out (_ibid._, p. 7) 172 hectares rented out by state organizations and state farms was deducted. The land rented out by non-farmers was taken to be 621,853 hectares (543,102 and 78,751). This figure is 27% of 2,294,555 hectares (2,294,727 - 172), or the complement of 73%. This proportion is used for making the estimates.

One obtains a proportion of 68%, instead of 73%, if one adds the figures in the following three columns in _ibid._, pp. 6-7: (a) "area rented from other," (b) "area owned (sic) on a share or partnership basis," and (c) "area owned (sic) on other basis" for the 13 lines where the data are shown by size of holdings, and if one subtracts from the sum of (a) plus (b) plus (c) for these 13 lines the sum of the same 13 lines in the column entitled "area rented to others on a share or partnership or other basis." (See also note 13 to this chapter.)

[11]See for example, Alfred Bonné, State and Economics in the Middle East (Second edition; London: Routledge & Kegan Paul Ltd., 1955), p. 126.

[12]See 1963 Census of Agriculture, pp. XXIX-XXXI.

[13]The over-all distribution of income in Table 4 on p. 159 could easily be revised if the data on rent earned (in column 3 of that table) had to be changed. This would involve recomputing the average incomes from all sources in column 12, and after adding the new average income figures in that column, recalculating column 13 directly from the new average figures and their sum in column 12. (Average rather than total figures can be used for this, since the number of families in each tenth of the distribution is the same.)

[14]Aside from the accuracy of the 1963 census data and their interpretation, there is also the question of the applicability of 1963 data to 1951 conditions. This question is likely to be less serious than the first because it is probable that the distribution of rent earned by farmers changed less than that of rent paid, and Appendix F shows that the change in the latter was apparently not too great. The reason is that, if tenancy increases, the extra land can be rented either from farmers or urban residents, and not all of the increase in rent paid by farmers should result in an increase in the amount of rent earned in the agricultural sector. Between 1951 and 1963 population pressure should have caused more tenancy among small farmers; however, to the extent to which they rented the additional land from urban families the amount and distribution of rent earned by farmers would be unaffected. The same would also be true if they rented the extra land from peasants pushed out by the same population pressure--peasants who move to the city are usually reluctant to sell their land--since the "landlords" in this case

would have become non-farm families. And neither would the distribution of rent earned be affected by the fact that large farmers probably increased the amount of land they rented from others-- since they purchased more tractors since 1951-- at least not if they rent from former peasants or other urban residents.

[15]See pp. 141-42.

[16]Since according to the 1963 Census of Agriculture, pp. 6-7, 73% of all farm land rented from others is rented from farm operators, total rent earned by farmers was taken to be 73% of the value of rent paid, estimated above at TL. 229 million. 73% of TL. 229 million is TL. 169 million.

[17]The distribution of land rented out by farm operators was calculated from ibid., pp. 6-7.

[18]See p. 26.

[19]Calculated from 1949 Village Census, p. 10, lines 107 and 104. The total number of villagers who left their villages in search of work during the year, less those among them who went to other villages, is equal to the number of villagers who looked for work in communities other than villages, i.e., towns and mining area.

[20]Calculated from the data on the number of villagers who look for temporary work in towns and mining areas (see preceding note), and the total amount of time that these villagers stayed in towns and mining areas. The total time was obtained as the difference between (a) the total number of man-days that members of farm families spent away from their villages in search of work, and (b) the total number of man-days that farmers who left their villages spent in other villages to work (shown in ibid., p. 10, lines 108 and 105).

21For the number of man-days, see preceding note. These data refer to 1949, however. They were adjusted to make them applicable to 1951 on the assumption that the number of these farmers, and consequently the number of man-days worked, increased in proportion to the increase in the rural population between 1949 and 1951.

22From data supplied by Etibank. The average daily wage per worker was TL. 3.35.

23The 97,500 workers who looked for work in towns and mining areas in 1949 (see note 19 to this chapter for method and sources), stayed away from their villages a total of 42.7 million man-days (see note 20 to this chapter for method and sources). From this figure 65/365 or 1/18 was deducted on the assumption that Sundays and holidays took 55 days a year and looking for work another 10 days. The resulting number of man-days actually worked in 1949 was increased by 4% (see note 21 to this chapter), in order to make it more pertinent for 1951, and then multiplied by the Etibank wage figure (see note directly above), to derive the value of TL. 119 million.

24In 1949 Village Census, compare the number of village shops and businesses on p. 10, with the number of persons working in each type of business on p. 12.

25Some might belong to absentee owners, but due to the small scale of these village operations-- where even brick kilns, the largest business in terms of average number of workers, employ on the average no more than five workers--their number is probably small. (For sources of data see preceding note.)

26Ibid., p. 2, line 3.

27By deducting the families in 1. and the number of persons in 2., it is assumed, for one,

that families who engage in both agricultural and
non-agricultural activities do no more than one
type of non-agricultural work, i.e., they either
run village shops, or work in local business for
paid wages, or engage in non-agricultural work in
their homes, with no overlap of activities among
families; and secondly, that only one member of
each farm family works locally for paid wages, so
that each employee represents one family.

[28]Ibid., p. 2, line 20.

[29]Among the activities included, the most important in terms of numbers of families engaged in
them are: (a) processing of forest products,
(b) weaving, (c) charcoal making, (d) processing
of reeds, and (e) transportation. Item (e) probably refers to the work of hamals (porters).

[30]Türkiye Millî Geliri, p. 28 and Appendix
Table 63.

[31]Before multiplying the number of families engaged in each of these activities by the corresponding incomes, the number of families was adjusted to make them applicable to 1951, since
they had been derived from the 1949 census which
applied to 1949. The adjustment consisted of
raising the number of these families in proportion to the growth of the rural population between 1949 and 1951.

[32]Ibid., p. 36, Table 25, and Appendix Table 63.

[33]1949 Village Census, p. 2, lines 3 and 4.

[34]The fact that village heads frequently are
among the larger farmers had been mentioned in
Chapter I as one of the reasons why the Village
Study sample includes relatively more large farmers than it should according to random sample
selection.

35Rental incomes have not been adjusted in deriving the total net income of these families,
although it was noted earlier that small farmers
in the Village Study pay less rent than the average small farmer in the nation. This adjustment was omitted in this instance because the
most logical assumption to make in relating supplementary incomes to other net incomes is that
the pressure to earn supplementary incomes is
related to the actual size of the farmers' income.

36By dividing the difference between the average
amount of supplementary earnings in the two lowest land brackets in the Village Study by the
difference in their incomes from farm operations
and rent earned, one finds the amount (in TL.)
by which supplementary incomes decline as incomes
from farm operations and rent increase by TL. 1.
At that rate the supplementary incomes become
zero when incomes from farm operations and rent
reach TL. 3,216. The land size to which this
income corresponds can be gauged approximately
by dividing TL. 3,216 by the average net income
per decare of the land bracket in which this income is earned. The result shows that supplementary incomes of this kind cease to be earned
by farms with roughly 250 decares and over.

37For details on the derivation of this distribution see note 36 to this chapter and note g to
Table 4 on p. 159.

38The class limit between the highest and second
highest tenth of all farm families in the distribution of income from farm operations and
rent in Table 4 is TL. 3,058, i.e., slightly below the income level of TL. 3,216 at which the
type of supplementary incomes derived by small
farmers ceased to be earned in the Village Study.

39Türkiye Millî Geliri, p. 21.

40Ibid., Appendix Table 49.

[41]Ibid., Appendix Table 49.

[42]From data supplied by the Central Statistical Office.

[43]See however, pp.146-47 above.

[44]See p. 24.

[45]The use of tractors should, however, not be taken as a sign of great enterprise on the part of the large farmers. The tractor program has been heavily promoted by the government; most of the money to buy them has been lent by the Agricultural Bank at very low interest rates (3%), and tractors, aside from increasing output, give the owners much prestige. Under these conditions the initiative for this innovation can hardly be assigned to those who bought the tractors. In other fields where improvements are much needed large farmers have apparently not taken the initiative. Thus, the shortage of irrigation and fertilizer in Turkey makes it necessary for large portions of the land to be left fallow every year. Aside from draft power, irrigation and fertilizer constitute the most basic needs of Turkish agriculture if output is to be increased. The evidence indicates that large farmers spend no more on these items than small farmers. When large and small farmers grow the same crops in the same regions, large farmers do not obtain higher yields unless they use tractors.

[46]For further details on the growth of inequality of agricultural incomes up to 1960, see Eva and Abraham Hirsch, "Changes in Agricultural Output per Capita of Rural Population in Turkey, 1927-1960."

APPENDIX A

COST OF CROPS, WORK ANIMALS, AND
NON-WORK ANIMALS, AND NET CROP
AND ANIMAL INCOMES IN
THE VILLAGE STUDY

[1]Op. cit.

[2]The winterfeed equivalents or feed units are 1.0 for cows, 1.2 for oxen, 1.0 for bulls, 0.6 for young cattle, 0.35 for sheep and lambs, 0.2 for goats, 1.3 for buffalos, 1.0 for horses and mules, and 0.4 for donkeys.

[3]Calculated from "A Survey of Grazing and Cattle Production," pp. 3 (Table 1), 4 and 6.

[4]The proportions of the total feed equivalents of work animals to the feed equivalents of all livestock owned in the Village Study, derived as explained above, were 61% for the farmers in the lowest land bracket, 45% for the second lowest, 41% for the third, and 24% for the highest land bracket.

[5]Reşat Aktan, in "Mechanization of Agriculture in Turkey," Land Economics, Vol. XXXIII, No. 4, 1957, p. 280, shows that 88% of the farmers in the Mechanization Study provided shelter for their machinery.

[6]Less than one tractor per farm for the highest land bracket, 0.05 tractors per farm for the second highest, and no tractors for the two lowest brackets.

[7]Village Study, Table 16.

[8]For the estimated proportions see note 4 to this chapter.

[9]Paul Stirling, "The Social Structure of Turkish Peasant Communities" (unpublished doctoral dissertation, Oxford University, 1951). In the revised and published version of this work, _Turkish Village_, _op. cit._, the details used for this estimate are omitted.

[10]The shepherd wages for sheep and goats reported by Stirling could be compared with the figures suggested for that period by Nafiz Erus, then head of the Agricultural Section of the Central Statistical Office. The two sources agreed in a rough sort of way.

[11]Village Study, Table 22.

[12]_Ibid._, Table 23.

[13]The estimated proportions of total wages paid respectively to (1) shepherds for non-work animals, (2) shepherds for work animals, and (3) agricultural laborers in the Village Study were 20%, 11%, 69%, for the lowest land bracket; 7%, 2%, 91%, for the second land bracket; 6%, 2%, 92%, for the third land bracket; and 8%, 1%, 91%, for the highest land bracket.

APPENDIX B

THE RETURN ON INVESTMENTS IN TRACTORS
AND MODERN EQUIPMENT IN
THE MECHANIZATION STUDY

[1]Interest on borrowed funds was not included with cost because the purpose of the calculations is to derive the return on investment whether borrowed or not.

[2]Turkey, Prime Ministry, Central Statistical Office, Agricultural Price Statistics, 1938-1951 (Publication No. 341; Ankara: Central Statistical Office, 1952), p. IV, and Türkiye Millî Geliri, Table 46 of Appendix.

[3]Türkiye Millî Geliri, p. 11.

[4]Tables 73, 76, 79, and 82.

[5]Tables 72, 75, 78, and 81.

[6]The average increase calculated directly from the Mechanization Study would have been 37% according to yields reported by village heads, and 35% according to the yields reported by farmers. But as noted earlier, the sample used in the Mechanization Study survey is not as representative of the relative importance of mechanized farms in each region as it should be. Because of this difficulty the relative importance of mechanized farms in each region was recalculated. The method used in making these recalculations is explained in section III A, pp. 197-98.

[7]Mechanization Study, Table 99.

[8]Personal information received from Reşat Aktan, one of the chief economists who conducted the Mechanization Study survey. In the calculations below the return for harvesting land for others

was taken to be 10%.

[9]Robinson, Letters, No. 36.

[10]See note 8 to Chapter VI.

[11]Robinson, in Letter No. 36, presents estimates according to which spring plowing takes 2/3 the time of fall plowing. This checks with estimates made by Nafiz Erus (former Director of Agricultural Statistics at the Central Statistical Office) that the season for wheat consists of 45 days in the fall, 30 days in the spring and 45 days in the summer.

[12]Robinson, in Letter No. 63 (February 1952), indicates that in the Çukurova plain in the Mediterranean wages were TL. 2 to TL. 3 a day. But in Letter No. 36 (August 1949), he gives a wage of TL. 3 for Central Anatolia. As the Village Study gives daily wages in 1953 of over TL. 4 a day, TL. 3 for 1952 would not seem too high a figure.

[13]A monthly wage of TL. 163 is shown to be the average wage paid to tractor drivers in the Mechanization Study, Table 42. For 75 days this gives TL. 408.

[14]This is estimated as follows: (1) The average number of work animals per farm in the Village Study was converted into feed equivalents (for the conversion into feed equivalents see p.183). (2) The feed equivalents of two oxen were calculated as a proportion of the figure derived in (1). (3) The resulting ratio was applied to the average cost of feed in the Village Study for work animals, which is shown in Appendix A above, Table 3. This gave the average feed cost of two oxen in money.

[15]The expenditures for animal shoes are arrived at by taking the average expenditure of TL. 12

per farm in the Village Study for animal shoeing
per farm, and dividing it by 3.35 animals, the
average number of work animals including donkeys,
owned per farm by the farmers in all land brackets combined. This gives an expense of TL. 3.58
per animal.

[16]This is pointed out by Reşat Aktan, op. cit.,
p. 278.

[17]In ibid., p. 278, it is indicated that mechanized farmers reduced the number of their oxen by
70%, their buffalos by 55%, and their horses by
50%. But no estimates have been made of the
savings in labor effected.

[18]The total investment in Table 105 was, however,
adjusted for the fact that the figure for Central Anatolia omits 67 families out of 580 for
lack of data. These families were added on the
assumption that their investment is equal to the
average in the region.

[19]Mechanization Study, Table 109.

[20]Information obtained from the Agricultural Bank.

[21]The figure of 12.5% is the one suggested by
Nafis Erus, former Director of Agricultural Statistics at the Central Statistical Office, as
the figure used for depreciation of machinery
for accounting purposes. This was corroborated
by Lester Brookner, American accounting expert
to I.C.A. in Ankara at the time.

[22]January to June 1956, p. XVI.

[23]Mechanization Study, Table 44.

[24]The smallest area cultivated per tractor, according to the Mechanization Study data, is 56
decares in the Black Sea region, and the largest
1,560 decares in Southeastern Anatolia. In the

Aegean and the Marmara regions it is around 200 decares, and in Central Anatolia and the Mediterranean regions around 550 decares.

[25]The area cultivated with tractors in each region was calculated by (1) deriving the area cultivated per tractor in each region (from Mechanization Study, Tables 5 and 65), and (2) by multiplying these data by the number of tractors in each region (shown in Agricultural Structure and Production, 1946-53, pp. 13-31). (The regional data in Agricultural Structure and Production were, however, adjusted because the provinces included in each region in the Mechanization Study do not entirely coincide with those of the same name in Agricultural Structure and Production. This involved moving the province of Balıkesir from region II to region III, Gaziantep from region IV to region VI, and Tokat from region VIII to region VII.) The sum of the areas cultivated with tractors in each region constitues the area cultivated with tractors in the nation. (Above the regional area figures are expressed as a percent of the national area figure.)

The national figure (the area cultivated with tractors in the nation), however, excludes region V (North East). The reason is that the Mechanization Study sample does not include any farms in that region. However, the understatement in the total area should be of only negligible magnitude; the number of tractors in region V constituted only 1.5% of all tractors used in the nation in 1952.

[26]Mechanization Study, Table 111.

[27]Reşat Aktan, op. cit., p. 277.

[28]Calculated from the data in Table 1, by deducting from the average income derived from tractors and modern equipment (of TL. 8,737) a cost of 3% on the borrowed portion of the investment

(3% of 60% of TL. 15,533), and then taking the
remaining income (TL. 8,737 less interest of
TL. 280) as a percent of the average equity capital of the tractor owners of TL. 6,213 (i.e.,
of 40% of the average investment of TL. 15,533
in this equipment).

THE RATE OF RETURN FROM INVESTMENTS IN
NON-WORK ANIMALS AND THEIR
ANIMAL BUILDINGS IN TURKEY

[1]See note (b) to Table 1 to this Appendix.

[2]The proportion of 8.6% was calculated from Monthly Bulletin of Statistics No. 64, p. 143, which shows the change in the number of each type of animal. Assuming that for each animal the change in value was proportional to the change in numbers, one arrives at this rate of increase in the total value of non-work animals between 1950 and 1951.

One difficulty in finding this rate consisted of the fact that the number of each type of animal shown in these statistics includes both work and non-work animals, i.e., both animals that create animal products and those that do not. For most types of animals one could clearly decide whether they produce animal products or not. Sheep, goats and Angora goats do; horses, donkeys, camels, and mules do not. But cattle and buffalos are used for work as well as for milk and meat, and the number of cattle and buffalos shown in the Monthly Bulletin includes both. Since, according to Agriculture 1949-1952, p. 16, the number of work animals in the nation increased only by the negligible proportion of 0.29% between 1950 and 1951, the increased number of cattle and buffalos in the Monthly Bulletin was entirely ascribed to non-work animals.

[3]According to unpublished data of the Central Statistical Office the total investment in livestock buildings was TL. 225 million in 1951, net of depreciation. Of this total about 50%, or TL. 113 million should represent buildings used for non-work animals, and the other 50% should be buildings used for work animals. These pro-

portions derive from a comparison of the data
in Tables 3 and 4 in Appendix A above, where
the expenditures on buildings used for work and
and non-work animals have been estimated for the
farmers in the Village Study.

[4]Türkiye Millî Geliri, Table 7, p. 20.

[5]Sixty percent is the ratio of the average cost
of work animals to the average cost of work and
non-work animals, estimated for the farmers in
the Village Study, if the costs for both types
of animals are figured exclusive of wage costs,
taxes, and the cost of livestock hire, which do
not consitute costs for national income purposes. These costs are shown in Appendix A,
Table 3 (col. 5, lines 15b and 16b) and Table 4
(line 9, col. 5) on pp. 182 and 188.

[6]Calculated from Appendix A above, Table 3.

[7]See p. 63.

[8]4% of TL. 2,040 million.

[9]Village Study, Table 28.

[10]Ibid., Table 16.

[11]The prices are partly unpublished data for
1953 obtained from the Central Statistical Office. To use them in these computations they
were reduced 20%, as it is suggested in Türkiye
Millî Geliri that the prices of animals on the
farms are, on the average, that much lower than
the prices gathered by the Central Statistical
Office, which are gathered in provincial centers. (See note (b) to Table 1.) The prices
obtained at the Central Statistical Office (as
well as the data in the Village Study) were sufficiently detailed so that the value of male,
female and young animals could be computed separately for each type of animal.

[12]The average is weighted according to the relative number of farms in each land bracket in the nation rather than the relative number in the Village Study in which the sample included too many large farms.

[13]Appendix A, Table 3, on p.182 above.

[14]Calculated from Türkiye Millî Geliri, p. 20 and Appendix Table 61.

[15]By multiplying the expenditure on buildings used for non-work animals in Appendix A, Table 3, by two and a half.

[16]See Appendix A, Table 1, note e, on p. 178 above.

[17]The rate of 34% derived below would become 36% if the value of the investment in animal buildings were to be half as large as the value estimated here.

[18]Confidence in the reliability of the official data on animal numbers has also been expressed by Vincent Lindquist, American technical advisor to the Central Statistical Office from 1950 to 1955, who found a great deal of agreement in the numbers found in the 1950 agricultural census and in independent data gathered in 1952.

[19]By converting all livestock numbers in the nation in 1950 and 1953 into common grazing units, and dividing the results by the rural population during each of these years, the increase in livestock numbers per capita of rural population amounted to 6% during the three-year interval. (Calculated from the data on livestock numbers in Monthly Bulletin of Statistics, No. 34-36, p. 177; the 1950 census data on rural population in Annuaire Statistique 1953, p. 44; the 1953 rural population figure was interpolated from the 1950 and 1955 census figures--the latter shown in Turkey, Central Statistical Office,

1955 Population Census, p. 10--on the assumption
that the increase was geometric. The method and
sources of converting the livestock data into
grazing units is explained on p. 67   note b to
Table 2.)

20Türkiye Millî Geliri, pp. 17-19.

21The derivation of these formulas is shown in
ibid., Appendix Table 47. The table shows that
the assumption of one offspring a year is made
for all milk-giving cows, buffalo cows, sheep,
goats, and Angora goats.
    These assumptions were questioned, for ex-
ample, by Marvel L. Baker, at the time Professor
of Animal Husbandry at the University of Nebraska,
and Dean of the University of Nebraska Faculty
in Turkey from 1955-57, in conversation with the
author.

22This is strongly brought out in a "Report of
A Committee to Consider the Livestock Pasture
and Feed Problem in Turkey," appended to Martin
Hansmeier, "Report and Recommendations Concerning
Crops and Soils in Turkey," p. 85. The report
is based on a committee meeting held in February
1951, and states: "All members of the committee
were of the opinion that a considerable increase
in the production of all animal products would
be possible in Turkey, provided the number of
animals on pastures could be adjusted to the
proper carrying capacity of those pastures."

23Between 1948 and 1958 the trend value of the
output of animal products in constant 1948 prices
(including the value of additions to the stock
of animals) increased 33%, and the livestock numbers that produce animal products (expressed in
common grazing units) 24%. (Sources of the value
of animal products and the increase in stock are
Türkiye Millî Geliri, Appendix Table 5 for the
years 1948-51, and unpublished data obtained

from the Central Statistical Office for the
years 1952-58. For the source of livestock data
and the method of converting them into common
grazing units, see p. 67, Table 2, note b.

[24]For a discussion of the fact that this overestimate increased during the 1950's and the effect of this increase on the trend in agricultural output during this period, see Eva and
Abraham Hirsch, "Changes in Agricultural Output
per Capita of Rural Population in Turkey, 1927-60."

ANALYSIS OF THE SHARE OF DIFFERENT FACTORS
RESPONSIBLE FOR THE HIGHER INCOMES PER
DECARE OF MECHANIZED FARMERS COMPARED
WITH AVERAGE FARMERS IN THE SAME REGION

[1]The difference in the income per decare between
these two columns is not entirely realistic,
however, as the farmers in the Mechanization
Study also grow other crops than the four main
ones, and column (2) only takes account of these
four. But no data is given on these other crops
in the Mechanization Study, so that only the
four crops could be included in these computations. If these other crops could have been
taken into account the difference in the incomes
per decare between these two columns would probably be somewhat greater, mostly because the
"other crops" in the Black Sea region are higher
income crops than the four main crops for which
data are given in that study.

TEST OF CONSILIENCE OF THE 1952
FALL SURVEY ON THE
DISTRIBUTION OF LAND OPERATED

[1]In 1950 Agricultural Census Results.

[2]1950 Census of Agriculture, p. 3.

[3]Ibid., Table 8. These data refer to the fall of 1952.

[4]The sum of the area sown, fallow land, vineyards, orchards and gardens, and olive groves in 1952. (Agricultural Structure and Production, 1946-53, p. 3.)

[5]That the two results were, in fact, independently derived, i.e., that no attempt was made to force agreement between them, was confirmed by Vincent Lindquist, American Technical Advisor to the Central Statistical Office between 1951 and 1955, in a letter to the author.

[6]The foreword to the 1950 Census of Agriculture (p. 3) states that the 1952 Fall Survey from which the data on the distribution of land operated are derived, consisted of a sample of 4,800 families this would make a sample of 1/526. In the detailed tables on the distribution of land operated (1950 Agriculture Census Results, pp. 124-35) all figures are multiples of 600, suggesting that the number of farms in the final data was somewhat smaller.

[7]This is done by comparing the data on the total land area included in the sample of the distribution of land operated for each province in ibid., p. 134, with the total of the area sown, fallow land, orchards, vineyards and gardens and olive

groves for each of the same provinces in <u>Agricultural Structure and Production, 1946-53</u>, pp. 3-4.

[8]The average discrepancy was 1,520 thousand decares per province, which is about 50% of the average land area cultivated in each province.

[9]For example, with a sample of 1/600, the omission or inclusion in the sample of three farms of 1,667 decares each could cause the land area in the province to be too large or too small by 1 million decares.

[10]On balance the understatements for the 18 provinces with incomes per decare of less than the average of TL. 45 is 26,430,000 decares, and the overstatements of the 10 provinces whose income per decare is greater than TL. 45 is 28,660,000 decares. The average gross crop and animal income per decare of cultivated land in the nation of TL. 45 is computed from the following sources: The data on gross crop and animal incomes are taken from <u>Türkiye Zirai İstihsal Kıymeti</u>, p. 4, where they are given by provinces, and were arranged by regions according to the classification in <u>Agricultural Structure and Production</u>. The total area of land cultivated is shown in <u>Agricultural Structure and Production, 1946-53</u>, pp. 3-4, and includes area sown, fallow land, orchards and gardens and olive groves.

[11]Independent farms are large farms that are not part of a village, i.e., do not pay any village taxes. Their numbers are shown in <u>1950 Agricultural Census Results</u>, pp. 2-3.

[12]Unpublished data based on results of the 1950 census of agriculture. The number of these farms is probably based on the same data as those on the independent large farms.

[13]The arithmetic mean farm income in Chapter VIII, Table 1, p. 124 (on the distribution of gross

crop and animal incomes) is TL. 3,797. However,
if this mean income is computed directly from the
total crop and animal income of TL. 8,274 million
(from Türkiye Zirai İstihsal Kıymeti 1952, p. 4)
and the total number of farms in the distribution of land operated which comprises 2,528 thousand families (from 1950 Agricultural Census Results, p. 134), the mean is TL. 3,173. Thus the
mean in Table 1 of Chapter VIII is 16% too high.

[14]Since the sampling error of small farms should
be much smaller than that of medium size farms,
the probability is much greater that the medium
size farms are included in the sample in provinces with too high an income per decare than
that this should be the case for the small farms.

[15]The mean crop income in Chapter VI, Table 2, is
TL. 2,456 per farm. But when the total crop income in the nation of TL. 5,363 million (from
Türkiye Zirai İstihsal Kıymeti 1952, p. 4) is
divided by the total number of farms (from 1950
Agricultural Census Results, p. 134) the mean
crop income per farm is TL. 2,122. Thus the mean
in Chapter VI, Table 2, is about 16% too high.

[16]See p.227-28. The comparison here is similar to
the one described on that page except that in
this instance the comparison involves the proportion of farms located in regions with less than
the national average gross crop income per decare, rather than the national average gross
crop and animal income per decare.

APPENDIX F

NOTE ON THE POSSIBLE USE OF 1963
CENSUS OF AGRICULTURE DATA

[1]Op. cit.

[2]See note 4 to this chapter.

[3]E. g., the amount of land rented by large farmers could have increased and that of small farmers decreased and vice versa.

[4]The proportions for part and full tenants in 1963 were 25.6% and 4.4% respectively, and in 1950, 22.0% and 3.9%. (The 1950 percentages were recomputed from 1950 Census of Agriculture, p. 8, to exclude "livestock-only" families.) The tenancy proportions in the 1963 Census of Agriculture were derived indirectly from pp. 6-7 as follows: if (a) are the farm families who are not full renters, i.e., those who either fully own their farms or rent only part of them; (b) are farm families who rent all or part of the land they operate; and (c) are the total number of farm families; then (b)/(c) is the proportion of all farm families who are tenants, whether they rent part or all of their farm land; and 100% less (a)/(c) is the proportion of all farm families who rent all the land they operate.

[5]In recomputing the distribution of net crop incomes in Chapter VII (Table 3) with the rent data of the 1963 census, the distribution was first recalculated by the same method and with the same data as used before, except that land rent was omitted from cost. The resulting income shares of each tenth of farm families were then converted into lira (where the total income to which this distribution applied was taken to be the net crop income at factor costs, adjusted for both trend and the overstatement in cereal out-

put--estimated on p. 59--less total wages paid
by farm operators--estimated on p. 26).   From
the lira income of each tenth of farm families
were then deducted the lira costs of rent of the
same families which were derived from the 1963
census. (These costs were calculated on the
assumption that the total cost of land rent--
estimated on p. 142 --is distributed among each
tenth of farm families in proportion to the relative amount of land these families rent. The
proportion of rented land could be derived from
1963 Census of Agriculture, pp. 6-7.)   In the
end the lira incomes, net of all costs and now
net, too, of land rent, were reconverted into a
percent distribution.

[6]For the method of estimation see pp. 107-111.

[7]The ratios of the census data (p. 14) to the
official ones for 1963 [in State Institute of
Statistics, Annuaire Statistique de la Turquie
(State Institute of Statistics, Publication
no. 490, Ankara, n.d.), p. 203] are 92% for buffalos, 82% for cattle, 95% for goats, 83% for
Angora goats, and 85% for sheep.

[8]See pp. 133-39.

[9]See pp. 138-39.

[10]The lowest tenth of the farm families earned
4% of all animal income, compared with 2% in
the distribution implicit in Table 5 of Chapter
VIII, and the highest tenth earned 21%, compared
with 27%. (The distribution of animal incomes
implicit in that of crop and animal incomes in
Table 5 of Chapter VIII was derived by exactly
the same method and from the same sources as was
the distribution of both crop and animal incomes
in that table, except that in each step of the
computations, crop incomes were omitted.)

[11]Because of the extensive plowing up of pasture land between the early 1950s and 1963, one would expect that in 1963 animal incomes accounted for a smaller part of income originating in agriculture than in 1950.   Thus, this problem may arise not because the 1963 data are faulty but because the weighting problem is aggravated by using 1963 data.

Turkish Government Publications

Turkey, Agricultural Bank. Türkiye Zirai İstihsal Kıymeti 1952. Statistical Consultation Service Publication No. 1.

_____. Türkiye Zirai İstihsal Kıymeti 1955. Statistical Consultation Service Publication No. 4.

Turkey, Ministry of Economy and Commerce. Konjonktür. January 1941 and January-June 1956.

Turkey, Ministry of Commerce. Konjonktür. January-March 1958.

Turkey, Prime Ministry, Central Statistical Office. 1950 Agricultural Census Results. (1950 Ziraat Sayımı Neticeleri). Publication No. 371, 1956.

_____. Agricultural Price Statistics 1938-1951. (Zirai Mahsul Fiatları İstatistiği 1938-1951). Publication No. 341, 1952.

_____. Agricultural Structure and Production 1946-1953. (Zirai Bünye ve İstihsal 1946-1953). Publication No. 351, 1954.

_____. Agricultural Structure and Production 1946-1954. (Zirai Bünye ve İstihsal 1946-1954). Publication No. 363, 1955.

_____. Agriculture 1949-1952. (Tarım 1949-1952). Statistical Résumé No. 9, 1953.

_____. Annuaire Statistique 1953. (İstatistik

Yıllığı 1953). Publication No. 360,
Vol. 21, n.d.

_____. 1950 Census of Agriculture. (1950 Ziraat
Sayımı), Statistical Résumé No. 12/s:1,
1953.

_____. Monthly Bulletin of Statistics. (Aylık
İstatistik Bülteni). No. 19 (September
1955), No. 23 (January 1956), No. 29 (July
1956), Nos. 34-36 (December 1956, January-
February 1957), Nos. 42-43 (August-Septem-
ber 1957), No. 55 (September 1958), No. 64
(June 1959), No. 80 (October 1960, No. 88
(June 1961).

_____. 1955 Population Census of Turkey. (1955
Genel Nüfus Sayımı). Publication No. 372,
1957.

_____. Turkiye Millî Geliri, 1938, 1948-1951.
Publication No. 352, 1954.

_____. 1948 Village Census Summary Results.
(1948 Köy Sayımı Hülâsa Sonuçları). Publication No. 320, 1952.

_____. 1949 Village Census Summary Results.
(1949 Köy Sayımı Hülâsa Sonuçları). Publication No. 344, 1953.

Turkey, Prime Ministry, State Institute of Sta-
tistics. 1963 Annuaire Statistique de la
Turquie. (1963 Türkiye İstatistik Yıllığı).
Publication No. 490, n.d.

_____. 1963 Census of Agriculture, Sample Sur-
vey Results. (1963 Genel Tarım Sayımı
Örnekleme Sonuçları). Publication No. 477,
1965.

Other Publications

Aktan, Reşat. "Mechanization of Agriculture in Turkey," Land Economics, Vol. XXXIII (November 1957).

Burns, Arthur F. and Mitchell, Wesley C. Measuring Business Cycles. New York: National Bureau of Economic Research, 1946.

Burns, Arthur R. Comparative Economic Organization. New York: Prentice-Hall Inc., 1955.

Bonné, Alfred. State and Economics in the Middle East. London: Routledge & Kegan Paul Ltd. Second edition, 1955.

Eppenstein, Franz. "Die Ernährung des mittelanatolischen Bauern," Revue de la Faculté des Sciences Economiques de l'Université d' Istanbul, Year I, 1940.

Faculty of Political Science, University of Ankara. Economic and Social Aspects of Farm Mechanization. Ankara, 1953.

Faculty of Political Science, University of Ankara. Türkiye'de Zirai Makinalaşma. Ankara, 1954.

Food and Agricultural Organization of the United Nations. Turkey, Country Report. FAO Mediterranean Development Project, Rome: Food and Agricultural Organization of the United Nations, 1959.

Helburn, Nicholas. Some Trends in the (sic) Turkish Agriculture. (Türk Ziraatında Bazı Tahavvül Seyirleri). Ankara: Doğuş Ltd, 1953.

Hirsch, Eva. "A Method of Estimating the Distribution of Farm Incomes in Turkey," The

Journal of Development Studies, Vol. II
(January, 1966).

Hirsch, Eva and Hirsch, Abraham. "Changes in
    Agricultural Output per Capita of Rural
    Population in Turkey, 1927-1960," _Economic
    Development and Cultural Change_, Vol. XI
    (July, 1963).

_____. "Changes in Terms of Trade of Farmers and
    their Effect on Real Income Per Capita of
    Rural Population in Turkey, 1927-1960,"
    Economic Development and Cultural Change,
    Vol. XIV (July, 1966).

_____. "Tax Reform and the Burden of Direct
    Taxation in Turkey," _Public Finance /
    Finances Publiques_, Vol. XXI, No. 3 (1966).

Kazım, Riza. _Die türkische Landwirtschaft und
    ihre wichtigsten Betriebszweige_. Ankara,
    1935.

Knight, Frank H. _Risk, Uncertainty and Profit_.
    New York: Houghton Mifflin Co., 1921.

Makal, Mahmut. _A Village in Anatolia_. London:
    Vallentine, Mitchell & Co., 1954.

Morrison, John A. _Alişar: A Unit of Land Occu-
    pance in the Kanak Su Basin of Central
    Anatolia_. Chicago: University of Chicago
    Libraries, 1939.

Nickoley, Edward Frederick. "Agriculture,"
    Modern Turkey, ed. Mears, Eliot Grinnell.
    New York: The MacMillan Company, 1924.

Ricardo, David. _Principles of Political Economy
    and Taxation_. New York: E.P. Dutton, 1943.
    Reprint of 3rd edition.

Stirling, Paul. _Turkish Village,_ London: Weidenfeld and Nicolson, 1965.

United Nations, Department of Economic and Social Affairs. _The Development of Manufacturing Industry in Egypt, Israel and Turkey._ New York: United Nations, 1958.

West, Quentin M. _Agricultural Development in Turkey. Effect on Products Competitive with U.S. Farm Exports._ U.S. Department of Agriculture, Foreign Agricultural Service, Foreign Agriculture Report No. 106, January 1958.

Unpublished Material

Aran, Ali, Gurnipar, Nevzat, and Brandow, George. "A Survey of Grazing and Cattle Production in Erzurum Province," U.S. Foreign Operations Administration. Ankara 1953. (Mimeographed.)

Brandow, George E. "Agricultural Development in Turkey," U.S. Foreign Operations Administration. Ankara 1953. (Mimeographed.)

Flügge, Wilhelm von. "Untersuchungen und Materialien zur türkischen Volkswirtschaft," Sonderbericht zum deutsch-türkischen Handelsverkehr. Istanbul University, 1936. (Mimeographed.)

Fotos, Evans. "Land Tenure and Rural Organization in Turkey since 1923." Unpublished doctoral dissertation, American University, Washington, D. C., 1956.

Hansmeier, Martin P. "Report and Recommendations Concerning Crops and Soils in Turkey," Mutual Security Agency, Special Mission to Turkey, November 1951. (Mimeographed.)

Harlan, Wilbur. "Analysis of Wheat Production
     in Turkey," I.C.A. Airgram: TOICA A - 430.
     November 16, 1956.

"Mémorandum présenté par l'expert turque."   Re-
     port submitted to the Economic Commission
     for Europe, n.d. (Mimeographed.)

Oakes, Harvey.   "Final Report, Soil Survey and
     Soil Management," U.S. Foreign Operations
     Administration.   T.A. Project 77-143.
     Ankara, May 1952-May 1954.

Robinson, Richard D.   "Village Economics," and
     "Tractors in the Village."   Letters Nos. 36
     and 63 in, Letters for the Institute of
     Current World Affairs and American Univer-
     sities Field Service, New York,
     August 8, 1949 and February 15, 1952.

Stirling, Paul.   "The Social Structure of Tur-
     kish Peasant Communities."   Unpublished
     doctoral dissertation.   Oxford University,
     1951.

Turkey, Ministry of Agriculture, Bureau of Agri-
     cultural Economics.   Unnamed Village Study.
     (Mimeographed.)